Author Les Coop
was Mayor of Cre
Nantwich in 1996

About the author and his books

The Mayor of Crewe saved young Les Cooper's impoverished father from the workhouse when he returned from the trenches after the First World War. Little was the lad to know when he left the Borough School at 14 that he would one day hold the same office.

The author spent all his working life in Crewe Railway Works and his books portray everyday life from the late 1920s until the end of the Second World War. The first, **Over My Shoulder,** is written in autobiographical style through the eyes of a child and teenager experiencing the Depression at first hand.

Another's War is a semi-autobiographical look at the life of a young man growing up in a provincial railway town during the Second World War. Against a backdrop of world events, it tells what it was like to be an apprentice in a reserved occupation and to endure the air raids on Crewe. The book contains rare photographs of bomb damage in the town.

The settings in both works are described vividly and the characters are real people, though many names have been changed.

These two books were originally printed and published separately in 1996 by Crewe and Nantwich Borough Council and sold in aid of Cllr Cooper's Mayor's Charity. They are now published in a Léonie Press omnibus edition by their original editor and page designer, Anne Loader.

LES COOPER

THE WAY WE WERE

Incorporating
OVER MY SHOULDER
and
ANOTHER'S WAR

**An imprint of
ANNE LOADER
PUBLICATIONS**

ISBN
1 901253 07 4

© Les Cooper

First published in this omnibus edition
by the Léonie Press in May 1998

Published by Crewe and Nantwich Borough Council
in separate volumes as:
Over My Shoulder or The Way We Were © July 1996
and
Another's War © July 1996

Published by:
Léonie Press
an imprint of
Anne Loader Publications
13 Vale Road
Hartford
Northwich
Cheshire CW8 1PL
Gt Britain
01606 75660

Printed by:
Anne Loader Publications

LES COOPER

OVER MY SHOULDER

Contents

I dedicate this book to my late wife Dorothy
Les Cooper, 1996

Chapter One
Early Days

Aconfused pattern of sights and sounds combine to form my early recollections of life in a provincial railway town in the mid-1920s. I've only to close my eyes to feel the sun warming my body as I played along with others of about the same age amidst the sand and rubble of a building site, as the first Crosville bus company garage was built near to the two-up two-down terrace house in which I was born and resided for so many years. A recent visit to the area and a glance at the plaque above the building confirms the date: it was 1926.

The babble of children's voices is all around and imagination takes reign as many a castle is built and sand pies are shaped only to be just as quickly trampled underfoot. The noise of building work is coupled with the strident voices of the men as they work, pausing now and again with rough good humour to send us kids scuffling away should we venture too near for safety.

It was safe enough to play then, especially in the side-streets, for there was little traffic and most was horse-drawn. Bert came each morning in a spotless white coat riding on the footstep of the milk float, with Bess in the shafts, serving milk and sometimes buttermilk from the churn; and Harry, cracking his whip in the air as he made his round with fresh vegetables and fruit for sale. The man with the handcart crying "Watercress, fresh watercress" — I heard his voice but never knew his name — came at the break of day; and "Eureka" the ice-cream man, sitting sideways and ringing his bell to attract hoards of children to his van to sample his wares, a halfpenny cornet or a penny wafer — I can savour the taste of his home-made product to this day.

We never lacked supervision for Mam was always nearby or an older brother or sister engaged perhaps in more sedate activities, took turns to look after the younger children, as did the neighbours pausing from household duties to cast an eye in our direction, especially when we visited the nearby Park. Once there, we divided our time between the sandpit, the swings and communal rocking horse, or tiring of that, we frolicked in the lush grass under the watchful eye of Charlie, the park superintendent. There was little vandalism in those

1

days, and rowdyism was frowned upon; the Park was kept in immaculate condition and woe betide the child who strayed into the shrubberies — he risked a tap from Charlie's stick. The amenities were freshly painted each year in an attractive shade of green and fresh cold water was available from two taps with tin cups attached. Two toilets were provided, suitably screened, and in reasonable condition. With a few sandwiches, it was possible to spend most of the day in the Park in fine weather, while Mam did her household chores and waited for Dad to come home from work in the evenings.

Mind you, not everyone had work and the spectacle of men hanging about at street corners was commonplace. Men with thin faces, pale with sad eyes peering from beneath peaked caps, shuffling from one foot to the other, staring out at a world that offered them nothing, talking in muted tones and thinking only of where the next meal was

The author with his mother, pictured around 1928

coming from. I didn't understand this, of course — how could I at so young an age — nor was I aware that my own father, after a three-year bout of unemployment, had only recently escaped the dole queue, and that as a baby my milk had been heated over a candle. For attempting to eke out a miserable existence by selling laces from door to door my father's dole money had been stopped and only by the generosity of the Mayor of the Borough was he saved from the workhouse — and this after five years in the trenches, and home to a country "fit for heroes to live in" with four medals to pin to his breast on Armistice Day.

In some respects I was lucky for this was a time of large families and I was an only child. Mam had been a tailoress, and with a remnant bought for a few pence from the Market stalls, she made most of my clothes and some of her own, though all was by hand for she had no machine.

Memories flood back of the times I stood absolutely still as, tape measure in hand, she prodded and poked and used basting stitches to ensure the garment fitted. Finally, with a sigh of satisfaction, she would release me from my captivity to return to my childish pursuits. At such times I would stroke her lush black hair, which fell to her shoulders, and kiss her smooth cheek as a token of childish appreciation — a final peck and then I would be off to join the other children playing in the street.

At other times, taking me by the hand, Mam would take me shopping. This was always a treat, for it was rare indeed that I was not given a few sweets. "Gob stoppers" were my particular favourite — they would last for hours, changing colour as they went until, with a final gulp, they were gone. There were also coconut chips, banana and strawberry ripple, Walker's toffee, and stick-jaw, broken into pieces with a small metal hammer, tiger nuts, "swaggering dick" shaped like a walking stick and striped; and a whole variety of morsels to tempt all but the most discerning palate. Some of the sweets we knew appear to have disappeared entirely from the shelves these days.

Shops in Market Terrace, Crewe — note the avenue of trees

There were numerous small shops catering for the needs of the neighbourhood including a pawnshop with its traditional sign, which did a brisk trade from Monday to Saturday. There was a newsagent, greengrocer, delicatessen, confectioner and butcher, as well as a small Co-operative Store. Cheek by jowl with these, there was a small shop where gramophones could be repaired, a paint and wallpaper shop, and two cobblers — one of whom specialised in the repair of clogs and was appropriately named "cloggers"; also two barber's shops, one with the traditional red and white pole to which was attached an umbrella signifying that here one could get that useful article repaired — so far as I was aware, it was the only place in town that performed this unusual service.

Tea-time, and father would return home from work. He was a blacksmith's striker employed in the Railway Works which straddled the town. To save the few pence bus fare, he walked the three miles from the steelworks and arrived home filthy from his day's toil, to collapse exhausted into his armchair. Several kettles of hot water later, he emerged from the kitchen reasonably clean and refreshed to eat his meal. I usually shared it with him perched upon his knee and dipped my bread into the toasted cheese, while he complained, laughing, when he thought I had more than my fair share. Mam eating sparingly watched us with amusement, and on winter evenings when the oil lamps were lit and the fire burned brightly, we sat and talked and perhaps played a few games or gramophone records — and so to bed.

Weekends were special. In summer, walks in the country, with Father striding ahead and Mam and me striving to keep up with him. Perhaps it was the thought of a foaming tankard of ale that spurred him on! On arrival at a country pub, I played with the other children in the garden whilst Mam and Dad enjoyed a quiet drink and a pleasant chat with the locals. In winter, we enjoyed an occasional visit to the cinema and, if we were lucky, a bite of supper sitting at a table covered with a checker-board cloth in the back room of the local chip shop. Fish, chips and mushy peas cost eighteen pence for the three of us, and that included bread and butter. A glass of Vimto to wash it down cost a further penny each.

Friday and Saturday were Market days and the Market formed part of the main shopping area. Traders would come from miles around to sell their wares, also farmers selling dairy produce and fresh vegetables. The area consisted of the Market Hall, a large covered area at the rear, and also a large open area, known locally as "behind the Market" with a vast array of stalls selling everything it was possible to imagine.

Hordes of people congregated there and small wonder, for there were bargains galore, especially towards evening when the naphtha

4

flares illuminated the scene with an unearthly glow. The scents, the sounds, the raucous voices of the traders proclaiming the latest offer, the chug-chug of the engine that drove the steam boats, the swish of the swings and the whirr of the children's roundabouts, the thump of a boot on leather as the young bloods tried to score a goal at a penny a go — all these had a fascination for a young child, and a visit to the Market was an experience to be relished and never forgotten.

The Market is still there, it still attracts the crowds, and there are still bargains to be had, but somehow it lacks the character it once had. The characters themselves are also missing from the scene. What happened to "Wrap it up, Charlie" I wonder — he could fling a roll of lino towards the crowd and hold it rigid, shouting "Ow would yer like this up yer lobby?" Tiger and his bevy of bruisers who would take on all comers in the boxing booth? Blackie with his brown paper bags full of luscious fruit? Tommy the blind beggar, who sat on an orange box outside the Wedgwood Chapel and sold laces? The 'quack' who sold sulphur tablets from a cardboard suitcase and proclaimed them as a panacea for all ills? The Market Inspector, top-hatted and frock-coated, collecting the rents in the late evening, and the coloured man with grizzled grey hair who lit and doused the naphtha flares? All are gone now, and we shall never see their like again.

Chapter Two
Kaleidoscope

*I*nfluence to date had been of a mostly feminine nature. Mam, of course, together with cousin Dora who lived next door, and Maggie whose Dad kept the bird shop in the High Street, had nurtured me through early childhood and, apart from tipping me out of my pram once or twice, had done a fair job of it. Aunt Jane who had earlier lost a little boy through diphtheria, lavished her attention on me when she wasn't looking after Billy who was in his third year at school. Uncle Jack, quiet, studious, employed in the Loco Works as a clerk — a job far below his potential — was to make his influence felt later. Dad, rough, kind, generous to a fault except when he was in drink, when he became argumentive, provided for our needs from his meagre stock. His wages — forty-two shillings for a forty-eight hour week — left little for luxuries, and short-time working loomed. Rent was seven shillings a week, beer five pence a pint, and "Woodbines" fourpence for a packet of ten.

Neighbourliness was the keynote in those days, and community spirit was paramount in the face of adversity. Doors were left open with no fear of advantage being taken, and there always seemed to be the large, capable female who made her presence felt at funerals, christenings and weddings and at other neighbourhood events like the odd street party.

Our house was one of two larger ones in a terraced row of eight cottages. The smaller ones had wooden gates and fences, and ours had iron gates and railings. There was a hole in the fence which gave easy access to next door and Mam and Aunt Jane exchanged frequent visits to each other's houses, or in summer time, when flowers covered the garden in bright profusion, hobnobbed across the garden fence. A funeral at St. Peter's Church nearby provided the occasion for crowds to gather from far and wide. If the family was poor, the deceased was carried into the church on the shoulders of the relatives or neighbours, the undertaker in front, and the mourners in their best black clothes followed behind. After the service, the cortege proceeded to the cemetery in similar fashion. If you worked for the Railway Company, you joined the Budge Club which paid out £3 towards the cost of the funeral.

A horse-drawn hearse with coach to follow signified someone of substance and provided something of a spectacle — the undertaker in tall hat adorned with black crepe, and frock coat, and a sombre countenance sitting with the driver in similar attire up on the front seat. As they waited outside the Church the coal-black Co-op horses' plumes nodded as they pawed the ground and sent rivulets of urine spilling down the gutters. And then the slow dignified procession through the winding streets to the graveside. It was so different from the almost indecent haste with which the deceased is conveyed to his last resting-place these days.

Weddings were equally well attended. The bride in home-made gown — but none the worse for that — and wearing perhaps her mother's bridal veil, followed by her attendants bearing posies, the bridegroom in a blue serge suit and looking distinctly uncomfortable in a stiff white collar and shirt front. Then the "oohs" and "aahs" and "here she comes", the good-natured banter, the showers of rice and it was away to the reception lovingly prepared at home or, if they were lucky, at the Coffee Tavern or perhaps the Church Hall. As for the spectators, they had a subject of conversation for the next day.

Time passes slowly when you are young but at last Christmas was almost upon us. Children's noses pressed to the newsagent's window ablaze with decorations and a Christmas tree in the centre with all manner of toys for sale was evidence of that. Here's something new — a racing car at 3/11d. complete with driver crouched over the wheel — a most fantastic fort with drawbridge and lots of lead soldiers at a penny each or twopence if they were on horseback. A clown that rode a pig and rocked back and forward when you wound it up, and dolls that closed their eyes and went to sleep; dolls' houses with bright red doors and curtained windows; games galore in brightly coloured boxes; toy gramophones that played nursery rhymes — all could be had if you joined the Christmas Club. You posted your letter to Santa Claus at the Penny Bazaar behind the Market and hoped that Santa would not have run out of toys before he got to you.

That night, muffled and wraith-like under the lantern, a small group of townsfolk sang carols beneath the Christmas Tree on the Market Square. I gazed in awe at the tiny figure of Jesus lying in the Crib. Oh, what joy, for this was the eve of His Birth! Now all had dispersed and Mam had made cocoa for Santa Claus and placed it in the oven to keep warm, and I was safely tucked in bed to await his coming. But I could hear voices raised in anger, Dad's voice, thick, disgruntled, argumentative, Mam's tremulous tone alternatively pleading and

A snow scene in Exchange Street, Crewe

scolding — feet clumping up the uncarpeted stairs, more words, then silence and sleep came at last.

Pale dawn, frost upon the window pane. Rank smell of stale beer. Weight upon my feet, reaching, groping in the dim light. White pillow case bulging and crackling with promise of good things. Had Santa remembered? Someone moving about downstairs, calling softly: "Has he been?" Candle on the bedside cabinet, dimly illuminating the room, a warm drink, gulp it down and then pulling at the strings and coloured paper of parcels wrapped with loving care. Excitement beyond belief, such promise of happy days to come; and then at the bottom of the sack a sugar pig, nuts, apples and oranges — a feast to gladden the heart of a young child. It is Christmas Day and it has a special magic, like no other day. Dad stirs, half awakens, murmurs "Happy Christmas" and then sleeps once more. It will be late before he greets the happy morn, and will not hear the bells ring out in salutation. The fire burns brightly casting a ruddy glow about the tiny kitchen festooned now with garlands and tinsel softening the stark outlines of the shabby furniture — table, chairs, and sofa stuffed with horsehair. "Little Miss Mischief" gazes down from the wall and seems even more inclined to bang her drum now that Christmas is here. The chicken is already in the oven at the side of the Yorkist grate gleaming brightly in the firelight, and the struggle to provide such luxury is forgotten in anticipation of the feast to come.

The fire is lit in the parlour, too, on this one day in the year and soon we shall gather round the Christmas tree with multi-coloured baubles hanging from its branches and with the star on top. A carpet here and a mirror over the mantelpiece on which two dogs each with a hare in its mouth gaze down disdainfully on the scene. An aspidistra on the window sill, bright garish ornaments on the sideboard with a sepia-tinted picture of Grandad and Grandma in the centre. Two armchairs with velvet cushions placed invitingly by the fireside — a recent acquisition from John Noble's 20-week club, when it was your turn you had your choice from the catalogue at so much a week.

The sight and taste of that bird, cooked to perfection, is with me still and after the crackers had been pulled and Mam voted the best cook in the whole of Great Britain, we retired to the front room to enjoy the rest of the day. Dad had pledged abstinence for the day but did take a glass or two of sherry and a drop of ginger wine, and the turmoil of Christmas Eve was forgotten.

Should I appear hypercritical of my father's lifestyle and of his role as a family man in those far-off days, my criticism is rather of the social conditions which forced this upon him. His work, demanding in the extreme, caused him to perspire heavily, and he needed to replenish his wracked body with copious liquid refreshment in order to survive. Wages were poor and as I have mentioned earlier short-time working and redundancy were ever-present threats even to our meagre existence. His efforts to ameliorate our conditions were not always successful and sometimes placed even more strain upon our domestic life.

Betty came for tea in the evening. Eyes wide with excitement, she surveyed the Christmas fare. Santa Claus had not been too kind and perhaps her letter to him had been mislaid. She was a few years older than me and was one of eight who managed, God knows how, to pack themselves into a tiny cottage. Her mother, old before her time and ailing, spent most of her time lying on a couch. Betty, small, rounded, pale, with golden ringlets tied with bits of ribbon, smelled of carbolic soap and occasionally broke wind. I often shared her pleasure in dressing cardboard dolls with cut-out dresses from a catalogue. Now she wolfed her food, hardly speaking, and the pile of cakes and mincepies soon disappeared without a trace.

Afterwards, Mam and Dad joined us in our games, the blind man from around the corner brought his concertina and we cracked nuts and sang carols around the fireside until it was time to go to bed.

And so into the New Year and the exciting but daunting prospect of entering upon the portals of education and to explore perhaps other worlds beyond the mean provincial town in which I lived and might come to regard as the hub of the Universe.

Chapter Three
Schooldays and All That

So it was that, muffled in a blue overcoat fashioned by Mam with loving care and twisting a handkerchief nervously in my hand, I was taken a few hundred yards up the road, past Dougie's shop that served as a grocers and, as I soon discovered, also as a tuck shop for the school, past the Co-op shop from which wafted the aroma of newly baked bread, and around the corner to the Borough School.

Young Les Cooper

The school, built in the early part of the 20th century, stood as it stands today, between two streets with a row of trim little dwellings on each side with a bit of garden attached. It is of red brick with a caretaker's cottage at one end. The streets give access to the site of the old reservoir, called in my day "The Razzer". Part of the site now forms the Cumberland Sports Centre and some of it is given over to housing. The allotments which we often raided for strawberries when in season are still there. Part of the school

The author, second row seated, far right, with his schoolmates at the Borough Junior School in 1930

has become a Sixth Form College and is used in an evening as a Youth Centre.

The headmistress, tall and with sweet smile but features that elude me, welcomed us, and along with a score of others I was taken into the classroom where I was to receive my first instruction. From then on, I was to be processed, packaged and finally at fourteen years of age, released upon an unsuspecting world. Amidst the paraphernalia of infancy, the sand, the plasticine, the coloured counters, the paint and wooden toys, I fell in love for the first time with someone other than my parents. The teacher, Miss Brent, small, smooth-cheeked with twinkling eyes and with her dark hair pinned in a bun, held me in rapture. She comforted me when I was sad and feeling not a little homesick, brought me cigarette cards with pictures of animals and occasionally gave me a quick peck on the cheek. Mind you, she shared her favours amongst us all and I felt a first twinge of jealousy.

Playtime and we enacted our fantasies in the schoolyard. I was an engine driver with coaches behind to form a train. My jacket suffered as a result and Mam told me off. We played as children will with with enthusiasm — a cacophony of sound erupted round the playground only ceasing when the handbell rang out for us to return to the classroom. At other times we played in the shelter or peered through the railings nibbling a bit of toast or a jam butty that our mothers had given us. Dinner time and home to a savoury-duck and gravy with a bit of dry bread or a penny Irishman from the chip-shop. A lot depended on what day of the week it was and whether Mam had been paid or not: Fridays were the worst, she was down to a few coppers by then. Weekends were better, especially if Dad hadn't stopped off at the local. Rabbit pie was a great favourite of mine — a rabbit was ninepence from the fishmonger's, or a shilling if they skinned it for you. Chawl was a penny a quarter, and ham off the bone was twopence. A hambone would provide more than one meal; with peas and pearl barley you could make a good nourishing soup. Sundays were best though with perhaps a bit of roast beef with roast potatoes and Yorkshire pud; or maybe lamb with mint sauce. I often wondered why old ladies stroked the arms of the chair so frequently — I know now they must have spent hours wondering where the next meal was coming from!

As I grew older, I started to do a few errands for Mam, so long as I stayed on the right side of the road for it was busier now with more motor vehicles about; they weren't only tradesmen either, a few had private cars, a Ford or maybe an Austin. I'd go to the baker's for a loaf still warm from the ovens with a brown crusty top that tempted you to nibble little bits as you walked along. You had to learn not to nibble too much or you had a ragging when you arrived home. I wasn't allowed to bring the tripe or cowheel from Tripey Rhodes though — you had to cross over the railway bridge to get there. Funny, in later years we were to play a game — how to get out of town without going over or under a railway bridge — of course, it's quite impossible!

A partition divided the Infant school from the Juniors, and as we squatted on the polished block floor in the Assembly Hall, our prayers were interrupted by sounds from behind the partition, and I often wondered what it would be like on the other side. I was soon to learn, and from thereon my preparation for life began. The teachers were kind but far more strict and you received a sharp tap from the ruler if you misbehaved or failed to pay attention. Well-thumbed and ink-stained textbooks were provided and you learned to write with a pen. You concentrated on forming your letters properly, learned basic mathematics, reading out loud without making a hash of it, writing compositions in which you were asked to describe your Mam and Dad in lurid detail; and gazed with pride on all that red on the map of the world. I received full marks for an essay that described Mam in such detail that the teacher was able to recognise her without much difficulty at the School Open Day. We learned too all about English and World history but of the former I cannot remember ever getting any further than the Industrial Revolution. We practised drawing and painting, made table mats woven with coloured raffia, and did P.T. in the Hall when it was raining, outside when it wasn't.

Examinations were held two or three times a year and parents received a report on our progress — "could have done better" and "should work harder" seemed to be a feature of mine. The Medical Officer of Health or his assistant visited the school once a year, as did the school dentist — the nit nurse was a more frequent visitor! "Daddy Thompson" and later "Daddy Whitney" visited your home if you were absent for more than a few days, and woe betide you if you didn't have a good excuse. The tall, bowler-hatted figure in dark suit, with collar and pince-nez spectacles was enough to strike terror in the hearts of all but the most hardened truant. For all their stern appearance, I suspect they were kind and caring people.

One day, we were all taken into the playground to witness a most extraordinary event. We gazed skywards to see the ill-fated R.101

passing overhead like a huge bloated cigar, its gondola crammed with passengers. It moved ponderously across the sky with a noise like thunder, teachers and pupils alike watching awe-struck until it disappeared from view. Though unsuccessful and later abandoned I think we all knew then that the conquest of the air had begun in earnest. Soon we were to witness, and the more fortunate to participate in, a flight with Alan Cobham and his Flying Circus from the fields at Merrills Bridge at five bob a time. These were stirring times indeed and a time to relish the spirit of adventure that filled our thoughts and minds with the promise of a new age.

As a small child, of course, I knew nothing of the General Strike and of the Wall Street crash that was to follow, and how it was to vitally affect our lives. I sensed however the bitterness and hatred that followed and witnessed much of the struggle for emancipation that became part of our existence in a small provincial railway town. There were large scale lay-offs in the Railway Works, particularly in the Steel Works where steel ceased to be made and was bought instead from Japan. Much of this steel of inferior quality lay rotting for years alongside the railway line. As the dole queues lengthened and conditions worsened, the bell at St. Peter's tolled more often. T.B. became captain of the "men of death" and diseases like diphtheria and scarlet fever grew to epidemic proportions. Rickets became rife amongst children of my age. Long lists began to appear outside the Municipal Buildings, denoting the condition of those patients inside the Isolation Hospital; by their names a terse comment ranging from "Very Ill to '"Fair" or "Improving" and maybe "Comfortable" conveying little to anxious parents. I succumbed to scarlet fever but was not taken to hospital where children lay feet to feet in the over-crowded wards. Possibly because I was an only child I remained at home for six weeks isolated by a curtain steeped in disinfectant. I remained in my room until the disease had passed and the men from the Health Department arrived to stove and disinfect the house. The doctors, overworked and lacking facilities, coped as best they could and bills were forgotten or paid at threepence a week at the surgery or collected by the dispenser who took time off to call each weekend.

Dr. Black was a typical family doctor. At two years of age I'd nearly died of pneumonia. He called daily and when the crisis came it was touch and go. He left that evening not expecting to see me alive again. He recommended hot poultices on my chest and back which Mam duly applied at intervals during the night. Morning came, and he called again by which time the crisis had passed. He paused by the bedside and murmured "that a good nurse was better than a thousand doctors". For weeks afterwards, he brought grapes and other aids to recovery until I was well. We never received a bill!

He spent what little time he had in the community and liked a drink in the "Belle Vue". At odd times of an evening he would call to see us perhaps a little fuddled but always with a paper full of fish and chips to share with us beside the fireside before he toddled home to a less than understanding wife!

From the mean streets the struggle for the hearts and minds of men began. Community spirit was of the essence. The Salvation Army sent its warriors from the Citadel and performed wondrous deeds as well as cheering us with a march through the town on a Sunday and a service on the Market Square at night with a chorus of rousing songs. There were as many churches as there were public houses and all were well patronised — the one to give sustenance to despairing souls, the other an opportunity to drown one's sorrows in complete oblivion with no thought of tomorrow. The workingmen's clubs had by this time also opened their doors to

Trinity Methodist Chapel with Mill Street Schools to the right

the family man and provided home-made entertainment and refreshment at a cheap rate together with the joy of belonging and the opportunity to participate in such sports as fishing, bowling, billiards, darts and dominoes and the like.

Opportunity was also being given for education of the masses through such organisations as the Mechanics' Institute, the Workers Educational Association and the Technical School. Courses in such subjects as Economics, Current Affairs, Philosophy and Elocution prospered, and then though I as a young child could not understand such matters, there began to emerge a political as well as a social awareness of the factors that governed our miserable existence; and gently at first, the Wind of Change began to waft through the mean streets and cobbled alleyways of my home town.

Vague memories stir of being taken behind the Market to hear the late Manny Shinwell, that eminent statesman, proclaim Socialist ideology from a rickety wooden stall to the waiting crowds. They cheered and jeered, sang "The Red Flag" and the "*Internationale*", vowed vengeance on the oppressors, and went home to their hovels to contemplate the future with new hope. Going to the hustings really meant something in those days. Prior to and on an Election Day, we wore our favours — a scrap of ribbon pinned to our jerseys, red, blue or yellow according to political persuasion. There were not too many blues in my class and they came mostly from the posh quarter that lay over the Manchester Railway bridge and poked a tenuous finger into the countryside.

In later years, I was to be enlightened as to the meaning of those barely whispered words "Socialism" and "Communism", and it would be Uncle Jack, that quiet serious man who lived next door who would explain such things to me and influence my thoughts and aspirations in the years ahead.

Chapter Four
Church and Carnival

Dora had left school and was in 'service' at Alderley. It was a good place and she was happy enough there and had time off alternate on weekends. She was a Sunday School teacher at Wedgwood Primitive Methodist Chapel. One Sunday she took me there, and from then on I attended regularly at least in the afternoons and occasionally went to Chapel in the evenings. Mam was pleased, she and Dad had been married there, he with his football jersey and shorts beneath his suit, and after the wedding he played for Haslington Villa in a Cup Tie. He gave the verger half-a-crown and was broke for the rest of the week. Not an entirely auspicious start to married life.

Most children attended Sunday School in those days and I made lots of new friends. I enjoyed learning all about Jesus and singing hymns in His praise. The teachers were wonderful and taught us much about life and how we ought to behave as Christians. It was fun, too, especially when we were taken on the annual Sunday School outing, though I am not sure that I enjoyed appearing on the platform on Anniversary Sunday. Over forty stars on your attendance card earned you a book prize presented to you on a special day at the end of the year.

On the day of the Sunday School outing, surrounded by doting parents and with a cup and a label showing your name attached to your jacket, you took your place in the procession to the Railway Station. With the banner unfurled and the Salvation Army band in front playing a lively tune, we marched along, the Scouts and Cubs in their uniforms providing a splash of colour, and a lorry carrying the younger children bringing up the rear. Down the station steps and on to the platform where the train awaited, the banner was ceremoniously stowed aboard the luggage van, and then we were on to the train laughing and singing, parents bidding a fond farewell to their offspring; a sharp whistle, a hiss of steam, grinding and groaning, and off we went for a day in the country five miles up the line to Minshull Vernon, or perhaps to Worleston.

The farmer and his wife greeted our arrival and it seemed that all

17

Sunday School Anniversary, Wedgwood PM Chapel 1934

the animals knew of our coming — the hens clucked, the cows moo-
ed, the horses whinnied, the pigs in their stye grunted a welcome and
the dogs barked furiously to see so many invade their privacy. Soon
the stalls were set up with all manner of goodies and the games
began. Sack races, egg and spoon races, three-legged and wheelbar-
row races, and if you tired of that, a go at the side-shows with a bar
of chocolate for the lucky winner or just perhaps a good old romp in
the grass provided you avoided the cow-pats. And then into the barn
where a magnificent feast awaited — sandwiches, cakes and jelly
with lashings of tea or pop to wash it all down. Then as evening drew
on a tired but happy crowd assembled once again for the return journey, fond farewells and then home again with all of us vowing that it
was the best Sunday School treat we'd ever had.

How utterly sincere that Sunday School Superintendent was as,
with hands clasped, eyes closed, and his whole body shaking with
emotion, he prayed for guidance and pleaded that all children everywhere should receive succour in a troubled world. How firm his faith
as he proclaimed the Word of the Lord and his utter belief in the
innate goodness of mankind. And when "Now the day is over" had
been sung and the last notes of the organ had died away, he watched
us as we left the hall and sighed and no doubt pondered upon the

uncertain future that lay before us. Through the quiet streets, past the shuttered shops drowsing now in the afternoon sunlight, past the Town Hall and Municipal Buildings with its grey stone facade and the model "Rocket" perched upon its topmost pinnacle; past the Market Hall deserted now except for a stray dog, over the Railway Bridge shrouded in smoke from a passing train and home once more to a cup of tea or a glass of homemade ginger beer. It was thirsty work, all that singing. Mam sits dozing in the rocking chair, lost in reverie. She starts as I enter the room and looks up smiling. Dad has gone to bed. He always did on a Sunday afternoon. Tony the spaniel puppy that Dad bought for the price of a racing pigeon trots over to lick my hand. We talk for a while and then I brush Mam's hair. She likes that and finds it soothing. I tell her of the hymns we've sung at Sunday School and we sing them together, her voice rich and contralto, mine shrill and not always in tune. Soon it's time for tea and Dad is coming downstairs.

Mam knew her Bible. She was once accosted by one of the "Chosen Few" and asked if she ever prayed. She replied in the affirmative. "Of course," said the zealot, "your prayers are not heard, only those of the Chosen Few shall enter the Kingdom." "And are you going there, then," Mam replied, "because if you are, I don't want to."

Sometimes we would go to the Wesleyan Chapel for a change. There were so many Churches and Chapels, all different denominations. There was the Welsh Chapel, the Scots Presbyterian, the Congregational, the Baptist, Christadelphians, Methodist and Primitive Methodist to mention but a few. All had differing styles of architecture and all drew large congregations. The largest was Christ Church, now sadly partially demolished. You paid your penny and

Christ Church viewed from the Railway Company's houses

took your choice and if you didn't like any of these you could always join the Salvation Army — or if you wanted to contact the dear departed, the Spiritualist Church.

One has to understand the cosmopolitan nature of the populace of a railway town. Artisans and labourers had flocked in their thousands from all parts of the British Isles to build the railways in the early part of the 19th century bringing with them differing creeds and customs, all of which found expression in the architecture, institutions and general lifestyle of a population that doubled within a few short years.

The Railway Company dominated our lives and we were subject to its demands. Both gas and water were provided by the Company and many of its employees were housed in purpose-built dwellings near to the workshops. Many street names bear witness to this domination — Richard Moon Street and Frank Webb Avenue are typical, and there are many more. Both Richard Moon and Frank Webb were Chief Engineers and their names are commemorated on two plaques at the entrance to the Queens Park. Many of the houses built by the Company have gone now and have been replaced by offices: an exception perhaps is Gaffers' Row recently renovated and preserved as a perfect example of Railway architecture. Gone, too, is that part of the Railway Works which lay alongside the houses. Forge Street entrance with its magnificent gateway and clock tower is no more, and a D.I.Y. store and furniture store together with a car park have taken its place.

You could visit the Queen's Hall Cinema for a twice nightly or matinee performance and enjoy a double feature show for sixpence if you didn't mind being lifted off your seat as the 10-ton hammer in the Forge thumped an ingot into shape at regular intervals. But more about that later.

The Cottage Hospital Fete held annually was the event of the year and was preceded by a huge procession that wended its way through the three miles of streets to the Queens Park. All the Railway Workshops and the Sheds provided troupes of dancers, and magnificent they were in beautiful costumes followed by tableaux mounted on lorries or horsedrawn vehicles gorgeously decorated and illustrating every aspect of community life. First would come the Colonel mounted on a coal-black charger to lead the Parade and behind him the Co-op Band setting the pace with the bandmaster throwing his staff into the air so high that you wondered whether he would catch it again. The Mayor and Mayoress in an open carriage, he in scarlet

20

robes with a tricorn hat and she in a pretty dress with broad-brimmed hat nodding and smiling and waving to the crowds that lined the pavement and spilled into the road. The "back to front" boys turning and gyrating so that you didn't know which way they were facing, a jazz band resplendent in blue and gold, blowing their razzaphones and banging the drum so that the earth shook as they passed. The "Butterflies" with gossamer wings outstretched, their costumes so beautiful that they made you gasp with pleasure. The "Mad Hatter's Tea Party" mounted on a lorry with Alice consoling the Dormouse; Humpty Dumpty sitting precariously on the wall surrounded by nursery rhyme characters. Another troupe, this time schoolchildren in pink and white and carrying garlands of flowers; the street collectors rattling their boxes under your nose, shouting "Help the Hospital, all in a good cause!", Mother Riley pushing the pram with an outsize baby clutching a titty-bottle; the Cock Horse wheeling and whirling and quite out of control; a man in a top hat, frock coat and fancy waistcoat about ten feet high, above the heads of the crowds; another float in green and brown with the Teddy Bears enjoying a picnic. And now the Rose Queen — how lovely she looks, a crown upon her head and accompanied by her attendants she bows and waves to the crowds. Characters in fancy dress selling balloons, streamers and "Kewpie" dolls. And now the King and Queen of Carnival in a horse-drawn coach, regal yet grotesque with grease paint running down their faces in the hot sun. Pennies thrown by the crowds clinking in the roadway. The Scouts, the Boys' Brigade in pill box hats, the Cubs, Girl Guides and Brownies in their brown uniforms and woollen bonnets; and finally the Corporation wagons, the Fire Engine, and the Ambulance vehicles — all were part of the Carnival procession, for this was Mardi Gras and a day to remember.

Chapter Five
Queens Park

O ften during school holidays we would visit Queens Park, regarded as one of the finest parks in the north of England. It was, and still is, an oasis of beauty and tranquillity in the midst of an industrial town. It is very much the people's place of recreation and pleasure.

Its thirty-six acres of grassland was dedicated to the public by Sir Richard Moon, former Chairman of the London & North Western Railway and designed by Frank Webb, General Manager of the Railway Works, and a former Mayor of the Borough. Opened by H.R.H. the Duke of Cambridge in 1888, it served to commemorate two important events — the Golden Jubilee of Queen Victoria and the 50th Anniversary of the Railway's involvement with the town.

Now as a heat wave shimmered above the dusty streets, we tramped the three miles to our destination, laughing and joking as we went, Sam and Tubby leading the way with Lily and Francis bringing up the rear, and Maggie pushing the old battered pram with Jimmy the little crippled boy aboard — complaining when we went too fast. Down the tree-lined Victoria Avenue, past the Webb Orphanage where the children in their brown uniforms were playing in the grounds, and then through the wrought iron gates into the Park.

A slight breeze wafted a greeting from amongst the trees and gave some relief to us tired travellers. Past the Clock Tower and down the magnificent avenue towards the Pavilion and the Boer War Memorial: I wondered if that soldier standing to attention on the top

The Webb Orphanage in Victoria Avenue

22

of the Memorial ever got tired and sat down for a while when nobody was looking?

The flowers in gay profusion in their well-tended beds bowed to us as we passed and their scent assailed our nostrils. Birds chirped a welcome and from the lake the splash of oars and the raucous voices of children at play drew us in their direction. Soon we would join them and would enjoy our day, thinking little of the long walk home again.

From across the road by the imposing entrance to the Park there arose the workshops and chimneys of the Railway Works silhouetted against the skyline dominating the scene; and around the corner at the side of the Park, the well-known sight known locally as The Cinder Tip which masqueraded as a Swiss Alp being snow-capped by the slag and waste material which cascaded down from its peak. On its steep incline, the wagon made its way ponderously to the top to discharge its contents and retreat once more like a giant black spider deprived of its prey. On the opposite side of the Park was the Cottage Hospital which received its patronage from the Railway Company and voluntary subscription from the townsfolk. It snoozed now in the summer sunshine, its patients cared for by underpaid nurses and doctors dedicating their lives to the care of the sick and needy. Its many windows glinting in the sunlight concealed the trauma and anguish of another day upon its busy and over-crowded wards.

Pausing first to look at the first World War tank and the old field gun by the Pavilion we played on the swings, took a turn on the see-saws, romped in the lush grass and queued for a trip on the paddle boats. We pretended we were pirates sailing the Spanish Main with the Jolly Roger fluttering at the helm. Treasure Island, however, was wired around and we were forbidden to land. Later we watched the older children diving and swimming in the lake like so many seals. How we envied them a dip in the cool water. But had we not been warned? Diving and swimming in the lake were shortly to be discontinued owing to pollution.

I could never understand why Pat Collins' Fair was allowed in the Park itself on Carnival days for it must have caused havoc when the weather turned sour. The huge engines which drove the roundabouts cut into the turf and it would take weeks for the staff to return it to its former condition. Pat Collins did, however, donate the whole of the day's takings to the Hospital so perhaps that was compensation enough. I was taken to the Carnival once when I was a very small boy. Almost before the huge decorated floats had entered the Park, the

The Park was kept in immaculate condition and children could happily spend a day playing there under the watchful eye of the Superintendent

dancing had begun and continued all day in separate arenas. The troupes competed fiercely for a small prize, but the honour of winning was important.

Red weals appeared on the legs of the girls as they slapped them in time with the music. Then there were the dog shows, a flower show, a bird show, rabbits in cages twitching their noses and retreating into corners as small fingers poked at them through the wires. Ice cream stalls, hot potato engines, Gypsy Rose Lee who told your fortune if you crossed her palm with silver; stalls selling coconuts if you were not fortunate enough to win one; humbugs — best quality — at a penny a quarter, or perhaps you fancied a toffee apple, a bag of pop-corn or some candy floss. All this not so different from today except that the atmosphere was somehow not the same. Everything had a different meaning, a sense of purpose. Daylight fireworks exploded overhead, and gas-filled balloons with your name and address attached floated away — perhaps to far distant shores or merely to be caught up in the trees before their journey had even begun. Children clustered around the Punch and Judy laughing loudly every time Punch clobbered his partner or crying when a balloon, held captive on a piece of string, escaped and floated away.

Families picnicked on the grass, or queued for refreshments — pork pies, sausage rolls, sandwiches and perhaps a glass of real ale.

Evening, and the coloured lights in the trees and the Chinese lanterns crossing the main drive illuminated it with a subdued glow. Throngs of townsfolk jostled each other along the paths and across the bridges and beside the lake to take up positions for the huge firework display to follow. The fair, now ablaze with lights, engines pounding, was full of the smell of oil and sawdust, the stallholders' voices raised above the din to induce you to 'have a go': "three darts for a penny try your luck now!" The coconut shies, roll a penny, the rifle range — "Win a kewpie doll, all the fun of the fair!" The roar of the roundabouts, the swish of the steam yachts, the cake walk, the ghost train, the prancing hobby horses, their painted faces grinning at you inviting you to take a ride — "All in a good cause, Help the Hospital!"

Then, as the rockets soared into the night sky and exploded in myriad showers of coloured stars, the faces of the King and Queen in glorious majesty appeared, producing a fitting finale to the display. It illuminated the lake and reflected upon the upturned faces of the huge crowd. The National Anthem was played, and almost before its strains had died away, the crowds were surging towards the gates and to whatever transport awaited, or the alternative of a long, slow trudge home to reflect perhaps upon this happy day — a glimmer of light in the encircling gloom of everyday existence.

As a child, and indeed in later life, I visited the Park on numerous occasions. I saw it and savoured its magic whatever the season. In Spring, with a host of golden daffodils upon its slopes, and fresh green shoots emerging from their winter's sleep, the buds bursting upon the shrubs and trees with a promise of new life, I knew what Wordsworth meant in his famous poem. And then the glorious summers of my youth as I strolled along its gentle paths and over its grey stone bridges with Millie — or was it Edith — and lingered awhile in some shady bower or perhaps rowed on the lake's placid surface and took tea in the Pavilion listening to the band. In autumn, too, as the leaves began to fall, providing a rich carpet of red and gold, soft and yielding beneath our feet, the wind soughing gently in the branches of the trees, the brittle sunlight, and the scudding clouds with the threat of rain. And in winter — the lake frozen now except for a little pool where the ducks played and snow-clad slopes where we rode many a home-made toboggan. The frost makes intricate patterns on the windows of the Pavilion, deserted and with no band to play a merry tune. Tracks of small animals and birds appear in the virgin snow. A swan circling, graceful upon a current of air, is poised to land on the frozen lake — and then disaster strikes as it crashes upon the surface and skids along to finish in a tangled heap beside the bank.

Whatever its mood, Queens Park will always find a special place in my heart. It conjures up happy memories of my childhood and early youth as no other place can, and those memories have a magic all of their own.

Chapter Six
"Call me Sir"

He comes from the shrouded mists of time and stands once more upon the rain-soaked playground. The rain has eased to a steady drizzle as, clad in a shabby sports coat and wearing baggy grey trousers and a slouch hat, he comes towards us. His features are rugged, his eyes startlingly blue with little laughter lines at the sides. His smile is reassuring but there is a hint of seriousness too and a note of warning that this man will stand no nonsense from a foolish schoolboy who dares to try his patience.

I wonder what his thoughts were as he led us those few yards through the school gates and into the main school buildings? Did he share our hopes and fears for the future? I suspect he did. Here was a scene that had been enacted many times before — "Good morning, boys", "Good morning, sir" we echoed in unison. New faces — a new term. Here was the clay to be moulded into shape — to be fired, glazed and polished, and finally released for sale to the highest bidder at the auction.

The girls had gone before us and were accommodated on the upper floor. We would see them at play in their own school yard but would mix no more as we had in the lower school. We would listen to their songs and hear their laughter but their school life was a world apart, and only when the day was over would we once again join them in childhood games.

The form system had been introduced and we had been selected according to ability into A or B grades. Classes were large, often

Borough Senior School seen from Brierley Street which the author attended

numbering forty or more. A school photograph from around that time illustrates this point for two photographs were necessary to cover the whole of the class. Our hair was short, most had a fringe, and with the exception of two or three, all had holes in their jerseys. Families were large and the younger children had to make do with "hand me downs". One thing though, we were all scrupulously clean and a cleanliness parade was held each morning to ensure that we remained that way. A house system had also been introduced and prefects were elected as well as monitors for each class. We were divided into four houses — Trevithick, Hodgson, Webb and Atkinson, these names all belonging to persons who had given special service to the community. As well as the school badge, we wore the colours of the House to which we belonged and competition was fierce to win the School Shield which was presented at the end of term. Competition was fierce too to win a scholarship to the Secondary School and in this field we had reasonable success. It helped, though, if your parents were better off, for places could be bought either at the Secondary School or at the Academy, even if the child was not too bright. For the less successful, there was the prospect of an apprenticeship in the Railway Works if your father already worked there, a job on the Corporation or perhaps as a shop assistant — for the girls, a life in "service", a menial job at the local hospital or maybe a job in a clothing factory. A Secondary School education was therefore of vital importance.

Nevertheless, the curriculum was varied, and every attempt was made to ensure we reached our full potential. Sporting activity was encouraged and as well as the newly opened swimming baths, we also had the use of very fine playing fields. Personally, I was not notably successful, though I liked to feel that I could emulate Larwood on the cricket field and could run a hundred yards in a respectable time.

"Busy", so called because he always was, taught us Biology. To illustrate his lesson he would often bring for our inspection a cow's eye, a lamb's liver or some other part of an animal's anatomy. It was interesting and we made copious notes and drawings in our exercise books. "Tich", however, who was the smallest boy in the class, and extremely sensitive, usually fainted at the sight of blood, was carried out into the Hall, revived with strong smelling salts and spent the rest of the lesson reading latest copy of the "Boys' Magazine". In later life, he was to fight for his country on many a battlefield including Alamein and Salerno; unhappily he did not return. What were his thoughts, I wonder, when he witnessed that bloody carnage?

Then there was Billy, he hated water — a trip on the paddle boats caused him to turn a particularly vivid shade of green as did a visit to the local swimming baths. Yes, you've guessed it — he joined the Navy during the War and served with distinction in frigates and submarines. He was awarded a medal for gallantry — posthumously.

We had a love-hate relationship with "Chippy" the woodwork master. He was fat and balding, with a grey moustache. He wore a dark suit, a bowler hat and shirt with a stiff wing-collar. He rode a battered old bicycle which creaked under his weight. His favourite phrase was "You blithering idiot" and that was applied to most of the boys in the class. Acute frustration would cause him to heave chips of wood at the unfortunate offender with deadly accuracy. You learned to duck as the missile came towards you — I did, and a piece of wood went straight through the classroom window! I don't think he ever forgave me for that.

Punishment was administered judiciously but without undue severity. Some masters achieved considerable dexterity in the use of the cane, waving it above their heads and bringing it down with a whack upon the outstretched palm. It was never applied to the bare buttocks, indeed hardly ever upon the backside at all. The punishment generally fitted the crime and the cane was preferable to 500 lines — there was no malice on either side.

"Twitter" was aptly named. He had birdlike features and spoke with a high falsetto voice. He was continually in trouble, and when on one occasion, the master was absent for a short while, he watered the geraniums without leaving the room and emptied the inkwell all over the floor. He knew that retribution would not long be delayed — he received three strokes and we one stroke for aiding and abetting.

Then one day, the whole of the town's schoolchildren were taken to London, the majority of us for the very first time. We had two special trains and the organisation must have been a nightmare for someone. We visited Regent's Park Zoo and for a while everything went smoothly for our party. That was until Twitter plagued the gorilla with a water pistol. The creature retaliated by throwing everything in its cage, including its own excreta, with unerring aim in our direction. Not satisfied with that, Twitter then became involved in a situation far more dangerous. He leaned over a wall surrounding a pool containing several varieties of highly poisonous swimming snakes and proceeded to dangle his attache case just above the level of the water. A snake roughly three feet long and purple in colour slid over the top of the case and back into the water. A keeper pounded across and extricated Twitter from a highly dangerous situation, and told him in no uncertain terms that if the snake had bitten him, he would have had less than five minutes to live.

Twitter was somewhat chastened after that, but had not finished by any means. A visit to the "Big Cats" was almost a disaster, especially as he ducked under the barrier in front of Leo's cage and tried to rouse the animal by continually banging his case against the bars. Leo gazed disinterestedly for a while and then suddenly, with a tremendous roar, he bounded across the cage and with one paw tore the offending object into pieces, almost taking Twitter's arm with it. He was quiet after that and we had no more problems.

Visits were often made to factories in the area to look at methods

of production and in some cases to sample the products. It was always a pleasure to visit the Milk Factory for instance, where we were given a glass of ice cold milk and a pound of delicious Cheshire cheese to take home. I would hazard a guess that less than half survived the journey home. Interesting, too, was a visit to the Tannery, the Salt Works, and of course, more importantly, the Railway Works.

The Railway Works stretched some four miles across the town to the railway station forming a Junction of massive proportions — it was in fact one of the largest in Britain. A visit there

Forge Street entrance gate to the old works and railway workshops

which extended over a whole day was of supreme importance because many of the pupils would almost certainly be employed there after leaving school. The premises could be entered by one of several gates, the most important being the Queen's Park entrance, the Deviation, and Goddard Street gates.

The Paint Shop where the locomotives came after they had been built or repaired, was of massive proportions. Interesting rather from our point of view was the number of old locomotives stored there, and these included the "Cornwall", the "Hardwicke" and the "Lion" together with a reproduction of Stephenson's "Rocket". Numerous other locomotives like the "Pet" that ran on narrow gauge railway lines carrying iron ore to the steel smelting plant, were also on show, preserved in immaculate condition to delight the eye of the railway enthusiast and to fascinate the small boy whose dream was to become an engine driver. All was noise and tumult as we entered the main workshops. The Steel foundry with its furnaces converting iron ore into steel, the huge cranes carrying cauldrons of white hot metal spilling over into the black dust which formed the foundry floor. Sad that those huge furnaces would so soon cease to operate and those who tended them would be thrown upon the scrap heap. Nearby, the huge rail mill, now derelict, where the sixty and ninety foot rails had been rolled over many years — a grim reminder of all that Depression can mean. We entered the Forge where the ten and twenty ton hammers pounded the white hot ingots into shape. The noise was deafening. The men sweated and toiled and the whole place shook to its foundations; here indeed was Dante's Inferno, and it was with some relief that we came out: once more upon the Works' yard. Then into the heavy Machine Shop with its huge lathes shaping the steel plates into the frames and sub-frames for the locomotives. The roar of the machinery was deafening and concentration was of the utmost importance to ensure precise detail.

Through the Brass Foundry and Brass Finishing Shop, and into the Foundry. Many of the component parts were of cast iron and here the air was filled with choking fumes so that you found it difficult to breathe. It was not surprising that the death rate among foundry workers was so high. The Chain Shop with its grey ghosts stooping over their work in intense heat in appalling conditions — "Abandon hope all ye who enter here!" for this was surely the gates of hell. This was part of the price we paid in human life — in human dignity — for our Railway Heritage. The Tender Shop, the Machine Shop with its

The "Cornwall" built in 1847 and on display for many years in the Paint Shop at Crewe LMS Railway Works

batteries of lathes all churning out the nuts and bolts of the railway industry. The pulleys and belts driving the machinery whirred madly, and the stench of oil and coolants was sharp in our nostrils. How was I to know that one day I, too, would operate one of those lathes? Next we went to the Boiler Shop. You had to be deaf or daft to work there. Our guide tried to explain, but the terrific din made it quite impossible and carried his words away like chaff in the wind.

Finally the Erecting Shop in which I was destined to spend much of my working life. The huge 50-ton cranes with their massive hooks which could transport the largest locomotive between them like a babe in arms moved ponderously overhead and we stood amazed at the spectacle. Whistles blew, hooters sounded, a bell clanged. Men in blue overalls and cloth caps swarmed about the locomotives like flies around a jam-jar. Here was the very heart of the industry and outside, in serried ranks, stood the product of their toil. The black, two-cylinder locomotives, workhorse of the railways, smart red and yellow for passenger transport; 080s, 060s, four foot threes, every possible wheel arrangement you could imagine, all waiting to be taken to the testing pits and then via the sheds to feed the transport system — the lifeblood of the nation.

It seemed something of an anti-climax to write about it afterwards, but write about it we did, and you had to be singularly unimaginative not to find anything to say.

Chapter Seven
Earning a Crust

Dad hailed from a little village a few miles from town. He was one of eleven children, six boys and five girls. Grandad had a vegetable round which was his sole source of income. On Election days his cart, with Bess the mare in the shafts, was decorated with blue ribbons. Dad left school at the age of eleven and had only a basic education. He started work as a boot boy at a local farm and was paid three shillings a week.

Having been brought up in a village, he disliked urban life intensely but was determined for our sakes to make the best of it. He always managed, God knows how, to take us on holiday each year; usually to Blackpool and once to Great Yarmouth. We took "apartments" for that meant we paid for a room only, and the food which we brought in was cooked for us by the landlady. This was a common practice in those days. As a railwayman he had one unpaid week's holiday each year and a free pass which entitled us to travel free anywhere in the London, Midland & Scottish region. He was also entitled to a limited number of quarter fares, that is travel at a reduced rate — third class only, of course.

It was fun going on holiday and I suppose I was lucky — some children never saw the sea. Our pleasures were simple enough, a paddle in the sea, donkey rides, building sand castles and decorating them with the flags of the Empire, a trip to the Pleasure Beach — and then perhaps a glass of lemonade or in Dad's case a pint of best bitter. Then back to the digs and a pleasant evening in the front parlour with the "joanna" playing and a sing-a-long,with the landlady doing her best to see that everyone had a good time and would return there again next year.

Many townsfolk joined the "Congo", a type of benevolent society with premises beneath the old Congregational Church. It acted as a Savings Club and paid out twice a year at holiday times, usually July and Christmas. It also served as a burial society for members, with an agreed amount at death. There were several other Friendly Societies such as the Hearts of Oak and The Foresters, whose members received sickness benefit. The local Co-op paid dividends on purchases at around two shillings in the £1.

A charabanc outing in 1930

Dad was a bookie's runner and a pigeon fancier. Street betting was, of course, illegal but the prospect of half-a-crown in the £1 commission was not to be sneezed at, and he took full advantage of the situation — mind you, he spent a lot of time in the local pubs and often returned home the worse for wear. Nevertheless, we benefited accordingly, and I suspect that was where the holiday money came from.

As for the pigeons — well, he won several long distance races including the one from San Sebastian. The prizes were not large however and the upkeep of the birds was considerable, especially in the winter.

A loud knock on the door one morning heralded the arrival of the police sergeant who lived across the way. I looked at him awestruck, you had a respect for policemen in those days. He was a huge fellow with a bristling moustache and a helmet that made him seem larger still.

"Dad at home?" he enquired, and my heart sank. "No," I quavered, "he's gone into town, I think."

He came in, placing his helmet upside down on the sideboard. Mam joined us, a worried look upon her face.

"Nice day for the race?"

"Er, yes," said Mam.

"Always have a bet on the National," he said, nodding his head towards the helmet. Mam took the bet, glancing at it.

"Half-a-crown each way, eh? Best of luck, Sergeant, I fancy that one myself."

Then he was gone, a broad grin on his face and whistling merrily. He was a good friend to Dad after that, often warning him when the "tecs" (detectives) were in the vicinity. Conviction, of course, meant a visit to court and a £2 fine. The bookie always paid it, mind, so I suppose it was worth the risk.

Harry was a typical bookie. Fat, paunchy, in a blue suit and waistcoat with a gold watch and chain and a bowler hat perched squarely on his head, he would call on Saturday evenings with the winnings and his visit would be followed by a small procession of punters at the door to collect them. Numerous schemes were hatched for the purpose of cheating the bookie, including lightning telecommunication from the course minutes after the race had been won. Harry dealt with them all with equanimity and good humour and shortly after introduced the clock system which timed the placing of a bet and made cheating impossible.

It was amazing what some folk would do to earn a crust! One day Dad and Uncle Joe who had just joined the dole queue procured a white dog, painted black spots on it and sold it as a Dalmatian. Unfortunately, it rained later in the day and washed the spots off — if the buyer had ever caught up with those two likeable rogues, I shudder to imagine what might have happened.

The streets around us produced some remarkable characters.

There was "Itchy Coo" or "Sammy Scratch" as he was sometimes called.

Poor Sammy, he was a casualty of the social system in which we lived. With a fortnight's growth of beard and clad in filthy clothes, he would rub himself against the wall, grimacing at the passers-by and making unintelligible sounds. Alternatively, he would collect cigarette butts from the gutter and smoke them in an old clay pipe. He was very fond of children though and he would smile at us and proffer a humbug often coated with tobacco dust. We hadn't the heart to refuse it but usually dropped it down the nearest grid. Sammy slept rough most of the time, but refused point blank to go to the Workhouse.

Then there was "Georgie Porgie" who like the nursery rhyme character "kissed the girls and made them cry". He was 34 and had a mental age of six. He was quite harmless though and the folks saw to it that he was looked after. Amongst the female characters, there was "Sally Knock Knock" and "Dot and Carry" — so-called because she had one leg shorter than the other. They were boon companions, and there was a never-ending procession of clients at the door of the terraced house which they shared.

Some people, of course, turned to petty crime to supplement their income. They were usually caught within a short time and sentenced to terms of imprisonment. "Tiger" was a particular example. He was more in jail than he was out. He was a likeable rascal though and generous when he was in funds. He always aimed to be in jail for Christmas to enjoy his Christmas dinner. Eventually he became a "copper's nark" or police informer.

On winter mornings the Coffee Tavern would be thronged with men in threadbare jackets, peaked caps and mufflers round their scrawny necks, gazing into space and hardly speaking, as they dallied for an hour over a single cup of coffee. It was warm in there and the air was foetid with the smell of stale bodies. Afterwards they would stand against the wall in groups hoping that someone would provide a "latch-opener" — an opportunity to go into the Cheese Hall for a drink and perhaps a bite to eat.

Women would take in washing to earn an extra shilling. You could always recognise them by their rough red hands and careworn features as they stood in line to buy a quarter of paupers' butter or a sliver of cheese at the local grocer's shop.

Washing day for us was always Monday. The boiler was fired quite early and soon clouds of steam enveloped the kitchen until it resembled a hot house. The week's washing was boiled in soapy water and the wooden dolly peg was agitated vigorously. The laundry was then taken out of the boiler, rinsed and put through the mangle and you took a turn at the wheel to squeeze it dry. The washing was hung from a rack and winched to the ceiling with a stout cord, fastened, and allowed to dry by the fire.

It was pleasant to relax in the evenings after a busy day and sometimes we would visit next door. Here things were slightly different. There were anti-macassars on the couch and on the chairs, and the shelves were lined with books in coloured bindings and titles in gold lettering. On the wall in the parlour the "Laughing Cavalier" sought to follow you wherever you went, and there was a picture of "When did you last see your Father?"

On the mantelpiece in the kitchen, brass ornaments glinted in the firelight and in one corner a gramophone, around which Uncle had built a cabinet, had pride of place. It had carved legs and a beautiful floral design on its panels. Uncle was so precise in everything he did, even to chopping sticks. Every one had to be the exact length and thickness. His bald head was concealed by a cap which he always wore, even in the house, and he whistled tunelessly as he worked.

Hands washed and dried, he selected the records with care, wiping each one with a cloth. Enraptured we listened to extracts from Gilbert and Sullivan, or renderings from some famous bass singer of "The Trumpeter" or "The Road to Mandalay". Sometimes for a change of humour we would have "The Laughing Policeman" or "Albert and the Lion".

Apart from his work, and perhaps an occasional day's outing with Aunt Jane to some place of historical interest, Uncle Jack rarely went far from home. Relaxation he found enough in the things about him and in particular his carpentry. He enjoyed a pipe of tobacco and a glass of supper beer with Aunt Jane on two evenings a week.

On some occasions, always providing my hands were clean, he would allow me to browse through a volume of "Harmsworth's Encyclopaedia" or "The Guide to English Literature". In the years to come, I was to sit with him as the light faded and the firelight glowed to explore the works of the great writers, the artists and the philosophers, and all to our mutual advantage for I was young and keen but lacked the experience of life that he was able to provide

I loved and admired both my father and my uncle: one the complete extrovert with a bubbling humour and love of life — despite his many problems which he had learned to tackle in his own way — and the other with his vast experience of life, his love of the arts and the wealth of knowledge that helped me over the years to shape my own life.

Chapter Eight
Transition

The games we played in those days were many and varied and some survive to this day. One of the most popular was marbles and here again there were several variations. "Ringy" consisted of a chalked circle in which were placed your own and your opponent's marbles. The idea was that by shooting a marble at the circle, you attempted to remove all your opponent's marbles before he removed yours. I was never quite able to understand why the phrase "Ebbs Kilaw" was used, however, when propelling the marble towards the circle.

The way to accumulate marbles was to have a "marble stall". Uncle made me one which proved to be a great attraction. It had little brass numbers over the holes with channels for the marbles to run into, and was surmounted by a fretwork design featuring marbles. I very soon became the "marble king!" Chippy examined it one morning and murmured something about Uncle never having realised his full potential as a very talented craftsman.

In the schoolyard, under supervision, we played netball, rounders and cricket. There was always a danger, though, that some budding Bradman would smash one of the school windows or that the ball would finish up in someone's parlour across the way, so we were always glad of the opportunity to go to the local playing fields.

Outside school hours we played in the park, the streets, or sometimes on a patch of rough ground at the rear of the houses. Most games had a seasonal flavour. Kite flying in March, of course, then "whip and top" followed by "jacks" or hop scotch, also "Peggotty" which was played with two pieces of wood, one placed across the other and belted into the air by a stout stick. Hoops made of wood or iron were propelled down the street at speed by a wooden stick or iron hook; "diabolo" was a shuttle with a groove controlled by a piece of cord attached to two wooden handles. Cigarette cards which you attempted to flick against each other in order to win the greatest number, and then there was "yo-yo" which made its appearance about this time and later became the subject of intense competition.

Street games generally included "I Spy" or "Whip" which was a similar game except that you hunted in packs and shouted "Whip" when you sighted your quarry and afterwards made a mad dash to regain the "den" before he did.

In winter we made clay engines — stuffed with waste material soaked in oil or paraffin and set on fire, they provided warmth for our frozen fingers. We skated on the frozen ponds and made bonfires around which we crouched to enjoy roast potatoes or chestnuts. Late on Saturday evenings, we would visit the local market and return with a bag full of stale "whackers" — these were cakes or pies which the stallholders had been unable to sell during the day and let us have at a penny a bag.

Pranks we played in plenty. A favourite one was to fasten two door knobs together and knock at both doors. This was easy because most houses were terraced. Another was "tip tap". You procured a length of twine to which a button was fastened, a foot from one end. The twine was attached to the window frame by a drawing pin, and you retired to a safe distance to ping the button against the window with a tip-tap motion.

We had crawled over a wall to do this one evening, and for a while there was no response. Suddenly the door opened and out came a very irate lady brandishing a red hot poker. We scrambled back over the wall with the lady in hot pursuit uttering the most appalling threats, and we were sufficiently deterred not to try that again for a while. Some houses had very primitive toilets and these were serviced by the night-soil men during the early hours of the morning. One somewhat unsavoury trick was to fasten a feather on the end of a short cane and wait for someone to use the toilet. If the victim happened to be a lady the results were sometimes quite dramatic.

We scrumped a few orchards and raided the odd allotment but there was no malice in what we did, and I can't think that anyone suffered as a result. A clout with the policeman's cloak

Slaughter Hill, scene of a battle during the Civil War, which was a favourite playground for children from the Crewe area

39

usually acted as a sufficient deterrent when we became too exuberant.

We could rarely afford to go to the swimming baths other than in a school party so we bathed in a nearby brook. It meant crossing the fields in which there was often a somewhat irate bull, but it was worth the risk, and armed with a few sandwiches and a bottle of Granny Roberts' home-made ginger beer, we would spend the day there. At one point there was what was known as "The Manhole" which was quite deep, but even if you couldn't swim it was possible to dive off the bank and, provided you kept underwater for a short while, you came up in the shallow end. After our bathe, we would eat our sandwiches, drink our "pop" and relax in the hot sunshine.

Sometimes we would go fishing, not in the canals for they were too far away and we had no transport, but in the many ponds in the area. A long cane, a length of twine, a pin and a matchstick float with a jam-jar to contain the catch was all we needed. We would catch sticklebacks and other small fish and it was a triumph indeed if you caught a "Red Doctor" to show off to your friends.

On the occasion of the Silver Jubilee Celebrations we had a street party. All the streets were decorated with the Union Jack and coloured bunting and prizes were awarded for the best effort. The bells rang out and photographs of King George and Queen Mary appeared in every shop window. The celebrations went on from dawn until dusk and the pubs were open all day.

Old word charm: one of two cottages typical of the Crewe Green area as seen from Crewe Green church

The women laid out white tablecloths on long trestle tables and a splendid feast was prepared for the children. We gorged ourselves as never before, and after that Joe played his accordion and we danced in the streets. In the Railway Works a brand new Silver Jubilee Locomotive, resplendent in black and silver, had been built to celebrate the occasion, and the Mayor came in his coach to tour the town — it was a truly unforgettable experience which, despite adversity, we were able to enjoy and would remember with pleasure in the days to come.

Unhappily, early the following year, those who had wireless sets were able to hear the sad announcement that "the King's life was drawing peacefully to a close" and soon we should be in mourning for a monarch who had shared with his subjects the long and bitter struggles of the early Thirties.

I'd started to run a few errands for a lady who lived at the end of our row. She paid me a shilling on Fridays, and with that together with my ordinary pocket money, I tasted affluence for the first time! On Friday evenings we would go to the "Penny Pictures" at the local Church Hall. The show usually lasted about 90 minutes and would include a full-length feature film and perhaps a couple of cartoons, Mickey Mouse or Donald Duck. The place would be crowded and if the projector broke down, as it often did, there would be a great commotion and a stamping of feet until it was re-started. Afterwards we would go to the local "chippy" and have a penny Irishman — chips and peas. You paid a further penny if you sat inside and had a glass of pop.

And it is worth recording that on one such occasion, I fell in love for the first time. She was pretty with long golden hair, blue eyes and soft warm cheeks, and lips that were so inviting — her name was Rosie. Soon hearts with arrows piercing them began to appear along with all the other graffiti on brick walls and our names were intertwined. Older lads said I should try putting my hand up her leg, but I didn't see the point of that and I didn't think Rosie would like it either. I must admit though that I did begin to feel a bit queer especially when she came close to me and the kissing became prolonged.

One summer's day after we had been swimming, Rosie suddenly decided to reveal her all and wanted me to do the same. I refused, but that didn't stop some of the other kids running home to tell Rosie's parents and mine what was going on. I had a ragging when I arrived home but I swear that Dad smiled and there was certainly a twinkle in his eye. Well, the romance faded a little after that, and the episode was forgotten. I noticed however that the older boys and girls often went into huddles and whispered together. I had passed the gooseberry bush stage, of course, but I began to wonder.

One little raven-haired beauty used to pass messages to me

through the classroom window which overlooked the girls' playground. I became quite infatuated with her until I was told she had "nits" in her hair; perhaps it was true, but there again, it may have been jealousy! Alice was different, she was older. She rarely joined in our games but chose instead to sit and watch us at play. She was pale, with brown lustrous eyes and black hair to her shoulders. She was an orphan and lived with her aunt who was out most of the day and left her to her own devices. She wore a skirt and blouse that was too tight, and black stockings. She called me one day to sit with her. We talked for a while and then somehow my arm was around her waist. She suggested I went home with her and went to bed. I didn't quite see the purpose of that on such a bright, sunny day. But I would learn...

I went off girls after that and concentrated on more masculine pursuits. Sometimes we would go along with some of the older boys to watch the local football team. "Barry" would stand outside selling humbugs at a penny a bag. "Don't forget your humbugs," he would shout. "We shan't have half enough for the regulars!" Then we were inside cheering the team to renewed efforts. "Shoot, Swindells!" we would shout and some wag would reply, "Why shoot Swindells, shoot the lot!" and we were part of that huge swaying throng of spectators out to cheer their team and vent their feelings on the referee. Perhaps he symbolised the foreman who had given them a hard time during the week. Congratulations when we won, excuses when we didn't — we would live to fight another day Then home to cheese and bacon cooking on the trivet in front of the fire, there was no taste like it!

Summer afternoons, and we watched the cricket or, if we became bored, played games in the grass or read the latest copy of the "Wizard" or the "Rover".

We were great collectors in those days. Cigarette cards were a particular favourite. Most cigarette manufacturers produced them in series of fifty cards. There were "Roses", "Do You Know?" "Famous Footballers" — also Cricketers, Jockeys and Athletes. Birds, Flowers and Flags of the World were popular series, and one tobacco company produced some really beautiful silk collectors' items which have now become extremely rare.

There were numerous magazines, too, on the newsagents' shelves, and I was an avid reader. "The Wizard", "The Rover", "The Skipper" and the "Boys' Magazine" — I read them all, and we traded them with each other.

What powers of prophecy those authors possessed! Much of what they envisaged has come to pass. Did they realise that one day the Empire would cease to be and that one day Communism would reign supreme over large sections of the globe, and that the world would be divided into two separate camps, each threatening the other with a nuclear holocaust that could destroy us all? I think not, for theirs was the stuff of dreams — an innate belief in the goodness of mankind and the triumph of good over evil.

Chapter Nine
Leisure and Entertainment

The townsfolk were, and still are, singularly fortunate in being able to escape from an urban environment with all that entails into the beautiful countryside. When the weather was fine we would ramble for miles across lush green fields and down

Lodge keeper's cottage at one entrance to Crewe Hall Estate. It faces Slaughter Hill and the Bloody Brook.

leafy lanes unsullied by heavy traffic and virtually untainted by pollution.

The whole area known as the "Old Park" was paradise indeed for us youngsters as together we climbed over stiles, strolled over well-trodden paths, and on to "Slaughter Hill" where we paused a while to dangle our feet in the clear cool waters of the "Bloody Brook". It was said that a great battle raged there once during the Civil War and that the blood ran down into the brook, thus giving it its name. Several artefacts were in fact found there beneath the sandy soil so the story may well have been true.

On now to the Golf Links, an 18-hole course of some considerable importance. Here we sat for a while to watch the golfers clad in plus-fours and multi-coloured cardigans, intent on their game. Their shouts of "fore" echoed across the course, and sometimes we were fortunate in being able to retrieve the odd golf ball and were rewarded with a few coppers for our efforts. Most of the area was privately owned by Lord Crewe and consisted of vast tracts of woodland interspersed by grassland with here and there the cottages of tenant farmers nestling cosily into a rich backcloth of green and gold. Their latticed windows glinted in the sunshine and wisps of smoke from the chimneys coiled lazily into the still air. Here the sweet song of the nightingale, the thrush, the blackbird and a cuckoo in season all joined in a welcoming chorus as we wandered along the pathways taking care not to trample on the wheat and corn knee-high in the fields. A rabbit scuttled across our path and a pheasant peeped at us through the hedgerow; multi-coloured butterflies danced before us and the air was vibrant with the drone of insects. In a stagnant pond the frogs croaked and dragon-flies hovered above the water, their slim bodies in blue and gold performing an arabesque for our delight. How sad that in the name of progress so many wildflowers and so much wildlife has become rare and has even disappeared from our fields and hedgerows. How sad that our grandchildren may never experience the joy and delight of a walk in the country as we did — what a terrible price to pay indeed for so-called progress.

Dominating the Old Park stood the magnificent mansion of Crewe Hall, built by Lord Chief Justice Sir Randolph Crewe and completed in 1636. The Hall was restored and extended in 1837, but unfortunately in 1866 almost the whole of the interior was destroyed by fire. The rebuilding within the existing walls was entrusted by

Typical Estate farm buildings, Crewe Green. Playing children took care not to damage the crops

Hungerford, third Baron Crewe, to Edward Barry, son of the architect of the Houses of Parliament, Sir Charles Barry.

As schoolchildren we were once privileged to visit the Hall. We were taken in a coach through the Golden Gates and up the impressive driveway. We entered through the main entrance and went into the Hall itself. Much of the old stonework had been replaced by alabaster and marble during the Victorian period and the old leaded panes had given way to stained glass windows. Nevertheless it was, and still is, a most impressive building. We visited the lovely Chapel

45

once said to be haunted, and saw the Marble Hall and the Carved Parlour. At the rear, there was a lovely ornamental Cup which poured water into the lake which at that time was well stocked with several varieties of fish. The Hall is now owned by the Duchy of Lancaster and at the time of writing is occupied by the Wellcome Foundation Limited.

We were not allowed to wander on to the Estate, of course, though I must admit we often did despite the "No trespassing" signs. Blue Bell Wood was the main attraction and we would often return home with bunches of wild flowers that grew in profusion there. Mind you — you had to keep an eye open for the gamekeepers, particularly Keeper Slynn, a notorious character who was said to take aim at you with a well-primed blunderbuss. I only encountered him once and received a verbal ragging — he must have left his gun at home!

I have tried recently to walk once again along those well-loved paths of my childhood but have found it difficult, and in some cases nigh impossible, to find them through a tangle of barbed wire and undergrowth. The occasional rambler may still find pleasure there but for myself I met not a soul!

Keeper Slynn: drawing used by kind permission of Mrs Sharrif, surviving daughter of Walter Gladden, who used this picture on the cover of his book "Cheshire Folk."

Walking then we did a-plenty but we sought of course to explore new horizons. Transport was reasonably cheap. You could travel from the Town Square to the Railway Station for a penny and to the nearest village for twopence, roughly a penny a mile. Railway travel was comparable, especially if your father was employed in the Railway Works and had the advantage of a quarter-fare. In fact, one newly opened club frequented by railway folk was called, aptly enough, the "Penny-a-Mile". As a change from watching the Robins on a Saturday afternoon we would

Keeper Slynn's cottage on Weston Lane, now called Narrow Lane

46

sometimes be taken to watch Liverpool, Stoke City or maybe Manchester United or the City. The entrance fee to even the big grounds was not extortionate and we were allowed in for half price anyway.

The love of the game was important in those days both among players and spectators, and you accepted the result, win or lose, with remarkable equanimity and good humour.

For a small town we had an unusually large number of cinemas. There was the Queen's Hall, which later became the Plaza, and is now a Bingo Hall; the Palace, the Empire, the Kino (later the Ritz); the Grand (locally known as the "Bug Hut"); and a few years later, the Odeon.

Saturday afternoon matinees were popular with the youngsters. You paid twopence downstairs and threepence in the Circle. The show, usually of two hours' duration, was preceded by a sing-a-long — "Happy Days are here again" or "Here we are again" — whilst the lights were still on and the attendants could still aim the disinfectant spray in the right direction. Then as the lights dimmed, the bouncing white ball guided us on the screen over the words of lesser known songs, before the show proper began. You watched Tom Mix, Buck Jones and Butch Cassidy riding the range, and Gene Autrey the Singing Cowboy, then perhaps "Tarzan the Mighty" swinging from tree to tree and paying lavish attention to Jane whom he had found stranded in the jungle at the mercy of a cannibal tribe. A couple of cartoons and then out you went to re-enact the whole thing over again in the streets or recreation ground. In the evenings you paid sixpence for a seat downstairs and ninepence in the Circle. Sometimes there was a double feature film with Pathe News and perhaps a travel film but more often there was a single film shown twice nightly. Lengthy films or classics such as "Ben Hur" or "All Quiet on the Western Front" were shown once nightly. Children were not allowed to see films with an "A" certificate unless accompanied by an adult.

As a very young child, of course, I saw many silent films with stars such as Harold Lloyd, Charlie Chaplin, Rudolph Valentino and Mary Pickford. A small orchestra provided the music and the effects were sometimes quite dramatic.

The first talkie I ever saw was "Broadway Melody" and later I watched "The Jazz Singer" starring Al Jolson. We queued for hours to see such films as "Rose Marie" starring Nelson Eddy and Jeanette Macdonald, or Eddie Cantor in "Roman Scandals", George Arliss,

Tom Walls, Maurice Chevalier, Von Stroheim, Buster Keaton, and that wonderful duo Laurel and Hardy — these were great favourites, as were Marie Dresler, Marlene Deitrich, Joan Crawford and Clara Bow, to mention just a few. The cinema was in its heydey, and the silver screen was to bring a new dimension into our lives and improve our horizons beyond all recognition.

The cinemas themselves had a character all of their own. The "Kino" later to become the "Ritz" was owned and managed by the local Co-operative Society. Its shell-like diffused lighting had emblazoned over it the virtues — Charity, Equality, Fraternity and Liberty. Well, charity there certainly was, but it came from those who were often equally afflicted; fraternity, the sense of the community spirit in the face of adversity, yes, there was plenty of that; equality, there was little of that; and liberty — well, that was purely relative in a class-ridden society.

The "Empire" occupied a central position and was perhaps more comfortable than the rest. It attracted the better films and was always well patronised — queues would often stretch for several hundred yards along the street and many were turned away to return again the following evening. The "Queens Hall", as I have described earlier, had its disadvantages because of its close proximity to the Forge. The "Palace" too, attracted large audiences, and was comfortable compared with the "Grand" — which earned its title of the "Bug Hut". It showed third rate films, the only consolation being that you

West Street: site of Grand Cinema (the "Bug Hut") on the right

had your money returned if it rained on the tin roof. In addition to the several cinemas, there were a couple of billiard halls, a reasonably good library, and perhaps more important a very lovely Victorian Theatre, the Lyceum. Built in 1911 on the site of a former Catholic Cemetery, the Lyceum was said to be haunted by an old lady in grey. Several persons, actors, actresses and patrons claimed to have seen her on more than one occasion, flitting amongst the stalls, in the Circle, or sometimes occupying a box.

You "dressed" to go to the Theatre in those days, except perhaps for us youngsters, who usually paid our fourpence to go into the gallery or what was generally known as the "Orange Box". From there you could look down upon the assembled throng and pelt them with pieces of orange peel. Downstairs, in the pit, pit-stalls and circle, the seats were of red plush and the huge building was decorated in white, blue and gold depicting figures from Greek Mythology. We sat on plain wooden forms arranged around the Gallery. We couldn't see the faces of the actors and actresses very plainly from there, but the music sounded wonderful!

We particularly enjoyed the music hall turns and saw many famous artistes such as Max Miller (The Cheeky Chappie), Lucan and McShane (Old Mother Riley), Larry Adler (harmonica), Glenda Jackson, and in later years the late Richard Beckinsale, and Peter Adamson (Len Fairclough of "Coronation Street"). Some were established and some just starting out on their careers. The Terence Byron Repertory Company was famous for its productions at the Theatre, and the "Old Studs" (ex-Grammar School students) regularly played Gilbert & Sullivan to large and appreciative audiences. I remember vividly the time I stayed to watch "The Pirates of Penzance" until eleven o'clock in the evening whilst Mam searched the town for me. I shall never forget the hiding I received that night either — I was only nine years old at the time.

Outside the Theatre, the commisionaire dressed in brown frock-coat laced with gold and a top hat would shout to the crowds in the street: "Early doors — all the best seats in the early doors — seats in all parts, fourpence, sixpence, a shilling, one and six" and the crowds would gather to form a queue and be entertained as they waited, by a gentleman who played the spoons, or perhaps by the one-legged beggar with his War medals pinned to his breast who, cap in hand, sang to them in a cracked voice.

Travelling circuses often came to town. Barnum and Baileys or

Sangers were frequent visitors, and they usually stayed for a week with a once-nightly show and a matinee on Saturday afternoon.

It was rare indeed though for the circus to come to the Theatre. For one thing, it wasn't really equipped to take the weight of the heavier animals, particularly the elephants, and for another, there was the problem of transporting the animals to and from the Theatre. I well recall one Saturday afternoon when folk were doing their afternoon shopping at the rear of the Market Hall when, to their consternation, there appeared among them four elephants, one large male one female and two smaller ones. Lily led the parade as trunk to tail they plodded among the crowd, the *mahout* on Lily's back urging her forward with a large, pointed stick and the others coming along behind in stately procession. Then suddenly disaster struck as Lily decided to sample the fruit on Blackie's stall. She placed one huge foot on the stall which promptly collapsed and the fruit scattered in all directions. Gracefully, Lily knelt down and, despite frantic jabs from the stick, she proceeded to consume most of it. What she left, the others ate, and in a very short while Blackie's profits disappeared down the elephants' throats. Lily rose to her feet, trumpeted loudly as a sign of evident satisfaction and then proceeded once more towards the rear of the Theatre at the same stately pace as before, pausing only along with the male elephant, to create a new traffic island in the middle of the street.

We trust that Blackie received ample compensation for the loss of his fruit and that all concerned were satisfied with the outcome. One thing is sure — the elephants were! Incidentally, I don't think the Theatre had another circus there after that...

Chapter Ten
The Magic Box

When I first met "Wally" he was crouched over a collection of batteries, wires, crystals and what he described as a cat's whisker although at the time I failed to see the relationship. He'd erected a metal pole in the garden from which stretched a wire; and attached to the wooden box on the table, which contained the whole complicated arrangement, there was a pair of headphones. He placed them over my ears, and from them there emitted the most weird howlings and cracklings whilst in the background I heard music and someone singing in a high tremulous voice that came and went in the most appalling fashion. At times, it almost became a shriek as Wally fiddled with the knobs at the side of the contraption which he was proud to describe as a Wireless Set. Mam said it was Wally's new toy and perhaps one day I would make one like it. I couldn't say that I thought much of the idea, and I thought Wally was a bit queer, anyway, so I promptly forgot all about it!

I was to be reminded of the incident much later, one Saturday afternoon in May, when I passed the pub on the corner on my way to the newsagent's shop for my

Crystal set circa 1923, with headphones dated around 1922. By kind permission of Mr Alec Loveday.

51

weekly copy of "The Wizard". The magazine offered a free gift that week — a cardboard boomerang which I was anxious to get before the copies ran out. Besides, I was feeling pretty flush with a few shillings jangling in my pocket, the proceeds from errands I'd done during the week. There was a Dinkie model of a car, too, I'd saved up to buy and add to my collection. As you can imagine, I was feeling pretty excited at the prospect of new acquisitions and was whistling merrily as I crossed over the road.

The reek of stale beer assailed my nostrils as I glanced inside the open door and into the dark smoky interior of the pub. From within there came the sound of muttered conversation and the occasional harsh squawk of the resident parrot roundly cursing the customers or alternately calling for the landlady with cries of "Bugger you, Lucy" or "Shut the bloody door". Above the cacophony of sound however I could hear the measured tones of someone describing an event. There were cheers and the sound of a vast multitude engrossed in the spectacle they were witnessing and now shared with millions more throughout the country, through the medium of wireless. I paused, fascinated, as I realised I was listening to my first broadcast of the Cup Final.

Soon a vast forest of metal poles with wires attached began to appear all over the town. The crystal set disappeared in a wave of nostalgia to be replaced by the battery set, but for many the luxury of wireless remained a dream for the Depression continued to bite hard during the Thirties. Despite this, the sale of licences soared and those who were fortunate to have a receiver often shared their treasured possession with others less fortunate, and it was common practice on Cup Final day, the Grand National or other notable events for people to share the experience — a few bottles of beer, some sandwiches, a packet of cigarettes, and a pleasant afternoon could be spent by any number of people crowded together in someone's front parlour.

So far, the greatest single advancement to date had been electricity. We could only afford to have it in two rooms — the kitchen and the parlour — but it did mean that as a child I need no longer strain my eyes to read in an evening and as a consequence my standard of education began to improve. When eventually we had a wireless, whole new horizons began to appear. In the classroom, too, wireless began to make its appearance and as a result children like myself were much better able to appreciate the world around us. Unhappily for me that came only in my last year at school.

Wireless had the effect of keeping men at home. Where previously they had sought solace in the pubs, they now stayed at home more
and this had a marked effect upon the public houses which tended to
decline in number. Thus:

"As a single man I strode about
and freely spent my tin
But now I'm wed I stay at home
and simply listen in"

Except for Saturday evenings, Dad certainly stayed at home more
often and listened to the programmes. He particularly enjoyed boxing
and football on a Saturday afternoon. The football authorities began
to complain however that football fans were beginning to turn into
fireside fans. I didn't think their objections were justified however
and attendance at football matches in my town did not appear to be
markedly affected.

Perhaps I did not altogether appreciate what was happening but
wireless must have had a marked effect upon the hospitals where programmes of all descriptions brought solace to the patients. To those
in my town whose only knowledge of music can have been the pub
piano, or perhaps the gramophone, there came an enlightenment
beyond belief, and more so for the blind, the aged and the poor. For
some, but unfortunately not for all, came the promise of a new life for
which many had never dared to hope.

Suddenly a host of magazines began to appear on the newsagents'
shelves that sought to teach the average schoolboy how to make his
own wireless set, and at school dur-ing Science lessons we began to
learn a whole new vocabulary of words connected with wireless.
Typical of these was "oscillation" which conjured up a picture of that
horrible person next door who twid-dled the knobs of his radio to the
extent that he caused yours to emit loud screeching noises. Hearing her

Home-made three-valve battery
receiver circa 1924 with horn loud-
speaker from about 1923. By kind
permission of Mr Alec Loveday.

neighbour's radio for the first time, a little girl friend of mine exclaimed to her mother that next door's wall was singing. But if originally the wireless was regarded as a miraculous toy and perhaps later as a hobby, most children were more interested in the programmes and regarded wireless as no more miraculous than running water.

Fashions changed very rapidly as sets became much more sophisticated; no longer the purely functional set but those encased in cabinets became the vogue and the radio became a thing of beauty, an item of furniture along with the radiogram, to take pride of place in the home. The B.B.C. Aunties and Uncles were very fond of their millions of nieces and nephews and for us "Children's Hour" became a very popular programme. Way back in in 1925 there had been an Uncle Clarence but for us the most popular was Uncle Mac.

Instead of roaming the streets we now sat engrossed in someone's front parlour listening to "Larry the Lamb", "Toy Town Parade" or "Zoo Man". Some of us became members of the Sunbeam Club and proudly wore a badge. Perhaps the idea was to encourage us youngsters to be well behaved, to look for beauty in the home, the school and in the countryside: I'm not sure just how successful that was.

Then there were the alternative commercial programmes like Radio Luxemburg with the "Ovaltinies — little boys and girls" who if they joined the Club, could have their birthday greetings read out on radio, a procedure which eventually ceased because of sheer weight of numbers.

I vividly recollect going to a friend's house one cold winter's evening to listen to the radio along with several other children. The friend lived in one of the L.M.S. Railway Company's houses near to the Railway Works. They were trim little cottages with a small porch and were comfortable enough and adequate for the needs of the railway employee, and close to the place of his employment. There was a problem however and it concerned the toilets. The principle was simple enough — two huge containers which were hinged so that when one became full, the mechanism caused the container to tip its contents into the sewer below, and the empty one replaced it at the top. I sat there gazing at the moon when suddenly there was a tremendous roar as the mechanism operated and I sat transfixed with horror wondering what on earth I had done to cause such a commotion. The incident did not do much to enhance my enjoyment of "Children's Hour"!

LMS company houses for the railway workers were built near the Works: trim little cottages with small porches and unusual sanitary arrangements

We didn't have wireless until the mid-thirties, but it was a mains set, a Philco with shadow tuning which Dad bought second-hand — a new radio would cost roughly four weeks' wages. For a whole week I didn't go out at all in the evenings but sat glued to the set.

The silver voices of the announcers provided us with the latest news: Stuart Hibbert, Freddie Grisewood, Alvar Liddell, Frank Phillips and John Snagge. To amuse us, there were such radio personalities as Clapham & Dwyer, Flotsam & Jetsam, Stainless Stephen, The Western Brothers, Elsie & Doris Waters, Claude Dampier, the then young Gracie Fields and many, many others too numerous to mention. Mind you, the B.B.C. applied strict rules — there were to be no gags about clergymen, Scotsmen, Welshmen, drink or medical matters.

Perhaps one of the greatest exponents of dance music was Henry Hall, with his signature tune "Its just the time for dancing" and signing off with "Here's to the next time" he was to captivate radio audiences for many years to come. Then there was Harry Roy with his "Bugle Call Rag", Ambrose with "When day is done", Jack Payne "Say it with music" and of course Charlie Kunz with the then very young Vera Lynn as the crooner. All these and many more contributed to our enjoyment of music in their own inimitable, style.

There was classical music too provided by the several B.B.C. Orchestras bringing the facility to enjoy the music of the great composers to millions of listeners all over the country. A schoolboy was once asked whether he thought London was a city or a town. "A town of course," he replied, "for when the roar of London traffic ceases, we are 'In town to-night'". Preceded by the famous Knightsbridge March who can ever forget that particular programme, one of the most popular and long-running programmes of that period?

Current affairs programmes were very popular in those days and served to enlighten people to a marked degree. As for sport, I remember listening enthralled to the Farr and Louis fight relayed from the Yankee Stadium, New York. The Boat Race, the Grand National, the Derby and of course the Cup Final were annual events shared for the first time by millions of people, listening all over the country.

It is interesting to note that the phrase "back to square one" originated from the "Radio Times" which published a plan of the football field marked out in numbered squares to assist the listener in following the game. Cricket with Howard Marshall and later John Arlott became the feature of a summer afternoons' entertainment. Then of course for the gardener there was Mr. Middleton, and if you enjoyed a play, there were plenty to choose from. A favourite programme was the "Palm Court Orchestra" on Sunday evenings with an opportunity for the tired housewife to relax to the accompaniment of a concert of light music. Religion too was not forgotten with a regular 10.45a.m. broadcast on a Sunday morning and again in the evening with the "Epilogue".

Radio did much in those days to relieve the drab existence of life in a provincial railway town suffering under the effects of depression. It provided entertainment, it gave solace to the sick and needy, it provided us with an awareness of life not previously enjoyed by the masses and it pointed a way to a new and better lifestyle.

But the storm clouds were gathering, and as we twiddled with the knobs we listened to the arrogant rantings of Adolf Hitler and his propaganda minister, Goebbels. We heard the voice of the politician and perhaps realised that radio could be utilised not purely for entertainment but for other and more sinister means.

King George V broadcast to the nation during the Jubilee Year and said through the medium of radio "nation should speak to nation" — a noble thought indeed, but would the nations listen?

Early in 1936 we mourned the passing of the King. 'The King's life is moving peacefully to a close" the announcer said. It was the passing also of an era. And after three days in which solemn music was played daily, the funeral parade and service were relayed to us over the radio and the nation joined together in the final tribute. We were not to know then of the stormy days that lay ahead and that before the decade had passed the new King would have abdicated, the reign of George VI would have begun and we should be at war with Germany.

Chapter Eleven
Crossroads

I was now in my final year at school; it was time to take stock of my achievements. I had not obtained a scholarship and that fact would vitally affect my prospects. On the credit side I'd maintained a good standard of English and English Literature and a fair mark in Mathematics. I could recite thirteen verses of "The Relief of Lucknow", sing reasonably well and knew the capitals of most countries (perhaps that was because I collected stamps!). I also knew that King Charles hid in an oak tree and that Henry VIII had six wives, most of whom he had executed. I received high marks for Science and came second three years running in Metalwork. In sport I was a fairly good sprinter and could do the 100 yards in 10.7 seconds, and bowled a reasonably fast ball at cricket. Football was not my sport but I enjoyed watching it. In addition to these qualifications, I won two health competitions organised by the Borough Council, and was presented on both occasions with a five shillings token prize by the Mayor of my hometown. On the first occasion I bought a watch with an illuminated dial from the newly-opened Marks & Spencers branch and the second time I used the money to put a deposit on a secondhand bicycle from a local shopkeeper. The watch was still in good order when I celebrated my 21st birthday and the bicycle, on which I must have ridden hundreds of miles, I finally sold for a couple of quid.

The masters were very kind and considerate but were obviously used to dealing with somewhat unpromising material. One suggested I might at some stage try journalism and another took me on a week's holiday to Gronant in North Wales as a companion for his own son. "Chippy" continued to throw lumps of wood at me though he'd no need to convince me that my future did not lie in carpentry. Uncle Jack consoled me but I sensed his disappointment that I had not done better. As for Dad, well, he didn't see anything wrong with my following in his footsteps with the added bonus that I might serve an apprenticeship to a trade in the Railway Works.

When I finally left school I ran through the wrought iron gates without a backward glance and with a feeling of trepidation mixed with an immense sense of release. The trepidation persisted and the

*Fishmonger's shop in Victoria Street very much as it was in the author's youth.
He worked for a time as a delivery boy for a wine shop.*

sense of freedom evaporated as I contemplated what my future might
be in the harsh uncompromising society in which I was to be taught
to earn my livelihood. But there was no turning back.

Christmas came and went, and amongst my presents was a smart
pair of long grey flannel trousers and a belt with a brass buckle. I felt
quite grown up wearing them, but I stood staring out of the window
for an hour before I ventured out for a stroll. On my way I posted an
application form for an apprenticeship with the London Midland
Scottish Railway Company and several days later received an
acknowledgement. Things were improving, the Works were recruiting
a limited number of staff including apprentices, and I would hear
from the Company in due time; in the meantime, I felt the need to get
a temporary job.

It was bitterly cold as at nine o'clock in the morning I joined the
queue at the Labour Exchange. Muttering, coughing and spluttering
the crowd shuffled forward till at last we were inside. It was warm in
there but the air was foetid with stale sweat and rancid tobacco
smoke. I gave my name to a nondescript individual sitting at a desk
and after what seemed an age I was called for an interview. The lady
behind the counter gave me a tired look and snuffled through a series

of green cards. Selecting one she said there was a job for a youth at a bicycle pump factory six miles out of town. She saw at once I wasn't interested and in a disgruntled voice inquired whether or not I had any ambition. "Not to make bicycle pumps," I retorted. She flicked through the cards again and selected one. "Delivery boy at a local wine shop? Not much prospect, but if you're waiting to go in the Works..." I hesitated and then said: "I'll give it a try." She handed me the card.

Snow was falling softly as I left the Exchange and I pulled my jacket tightly around me to keep out the cold. The wine shop was on the outskirts of town so I took the short cut across the old Iron Bridge that spanned the Railway Works. The steps were slippery and my footsteps clattered noisily on the metal surface. I slid down the incline and came out into the High Street. Past the "Green Goddess" and the "Royal Oak" and "Neptune" on the corner, and through the mean cobbled back streets with their huddle of tiny cottages, soot-stained, and with windows staring at me blankly as I passed. Soon the snow would shroud their drabness with a white coat of propriety. I came to the outskirts. Here things were better, large houses interspersed with offices and a fair number of shops, a couple of hotels, a dentist, a doctor's surgery and at the far end just as you came out into the suburbs, a convent — the whole area had an air of respectability.

The wine shop, small but neat, nestled between a confectioner's and a dress shop. The window displayed a selection of wines and spirits and was obviously patronised by the better-off. I went in clutching my green card and introduced myself to the manageress, Miss Moores. She was small and neat, like the shop. Middle-aged, with short grey hair and lined features, she gazed at me appraisingly through pince-nez spectacles. She spoke quietly and exuded an air of refinement. She reminded me of one of my infants' school teachers.

At the rear of the shop a fire burned brightly in an old-fashioned grate and a clock ticked noisily on the wall.

"Hours nine 'til five-thirty with an hour for lunch. Six days a week with every Wednesday afternoon off. Wages seven shillings and sixpence a week minus fourpence for stamps."

She detailed my duties. "Wine delivery within two miles of the shop — no bicycle." She couldn't risk that with wine and spirits. "Light the fire, scrub the floor, clean the windows."

My mind was in a whirl — I nodded acceptance.

"Week's trial, start on Monday."

The snow fell more thickly as I left the shop, but I hardly noticed it as I trudged home. My first job — Mam would be pleased.

It was hard work but the exercise did me good and my relationship with Miss Moores improved on acquaintance, though she did carp a bit when I streaked the windows or the brasswork wasn't polished to her satisfaction.

The accent was on politeness to the customers and that earned me many a welcome tip. Most of the houses were large and had servants. Some of them would take me into the kitchen and give me tea and lumps of slab cake. I flirted a bit too with some of the younger maids but I had to keep an eye on the clock in order to avoid a verbal ragging when I returned to the shop. As the weather improved, I took my lunch break en route, sometimes alone and sometimes with Kathy, a secondary schoolgirl whom I'd come to know whilst doing the rounds. I became quite fond of Kathy and the romance might have blossomed if her Dad hadn't caught us together strolling through the woods one day with my arm around her waist.

Every Saturday morning I would take the week's takings to the "Junction" public house in the town centre. I felt that I was trusted by Miss Moores and the staff and I developed a sense of pride when undertaking the task. It occurred to me afterwards though that any prospective thief would be unlike-

Hightown Methodist Church, now demolished

ly to suspect a young boy of carrying such a large amount of cash.

After four months I became restless. I wanted a change so I took a job at a local mineral water factory. The wages were better — nine shillings a week and as much lemonade as you could drink. I particularly enjoyed making the grapefruit squash in the huge vat upstairs. Most of the time however I spent with the delivery van and it was pleasant sitting with the driver as we went to the outlying areas. The work was hard, mauling those heavy crates about, but it was only five days a week, so I had all weekend to enjoy myself.

One morning a buff envelope arrived and a directive to report at the General Offices of the Railway Company for an interview. There were eight of us and after completing a short examination paper we were told to report at the Company's hospital for a medical. The hospital was a lovely old black and white building next to the local swimming baths. We were ushered into a small room and told to strip to the waist. I looked at the others and my heart sank, I was the smallest of the lot. A rigorous examination followed and then we reported back to the General Offices. A fussy little clerk in a dark suit glanced at the papers — seven failed, one passed. He turned to me.

"Report at the Machine Shop offices Monday morning, eight o'clock," he rasped, and was gone.

My steps were light as I returned home. Here I was at fourteen and a half years old accepted as an apprentice fitter and turner into the employ of the L.M.S. Railway Company. Mam was delighted and went straight out and bought me a smart pair of brown overalls and a pair of working boots. When Dad came home, he hugged me close and his eyes glowed with pride.

The boots hurt my feet slightly and they creaked as I walked but nothing could disguise the pride I felt walking to work with my Dad that first Monday morning. We started early and he left me standing by the Machine Shop office to await the arrival of the foreman. The noise of the machinery was deafening and I felt disorientated and incredibly alone.

A bowler-hatted figure in a blue suit with a gold watch and chain approached me and after a few words of introduction motioned me to follow him down the workshop. He took me to the clocks, gave me a clock card upon which was printed my name and number, and explained the clocking-on and off procedure. He then took me to a small cabin where a stout individual wearing blue overalls and a flat cap sat crouched over a desk. George, as I later found out, was my charge-hand. He waddled rather than walked and had a large lump at the side of his neck which caused him to hold his head on one side. George was, despite his disabilities, a kindly soul who looked after the apprentices in his charge. He took me to a young dark curly-haired lad who was operating a lathe nearby and after giving instructions that I was to be noviced for a week in the use of the lathe, he left me.

The lad taught me how to operate the lathe and explained that I would be required to turn off three hundred studs per day if I was to what he called "make your time" — over and above that number I would receive bonus accordingly. My basic rate was six shillings plus four shillings war wage. The latter had some relationship with an award made during the 1914-18 war. Hours were forty-two per week. Towards the end of my first day "Tommy" gave me a cigarette. I wish he hadn't because I've smoked ever since. This particular one I treasured all day and finally smoked in the toilet at home. Mam caught me at it and I had a ragging. Dad merely enquired if I had any more.

You weren't allowed to smoke at work. If you did, you went to the toilets. This was quite an experience as I soon found out. You had to shout your number out to the lavatory clerk who took it down in a ledger. A report was sent to the office if you spent more time there than was necessary. It was quite a shock to find that the toilets had no doors, and the sight of some old codger with his trousers down and his belt around his neck appalled me at first but I soon got used to the idea. There were no washing facilities either at that time, so the trick was to pay one of the cleaners threepence a week and he'd provide you with a bit of waste soaked in turpentine which helped at least to get the really dirty stuff off your hands.

The foremen were very strict. No larking about and no irregular clocking — you could be sent home for a couple of days for that and if it continued you were sacked.

It was too far to walk home at lunchtime so I joined Dad in the Smithy for a cup of tea and a few sandwiches. Sometimes we would bring bacon and cheese and have it cooked over a hot plate from the furnace. In summer we strolled across to Queen's Park and sat on the banks of the lake to enjoy a picnic. This was all right as long as the swans and particularly the Chinese gander didn't want to share your meal — if they did things could become quite catastrophic for there was no denying them if they became determined.

And so there passed the first year of my apprenticeship. Every three months we moved to another machine or perhaps even another department. I met new friends and made a few enemies but that was the way of life. I joined the Union, sixpence a fortnight with a blue card. I contracted to pay a penny a week to Webb Orphanage and joined the Works insurance scheme. You learned all the tricks of the trade and rapidly became part of the system. After seven years you became a tradesman, and after that — well, it was largely up to you.

Chapter Twelve
Apprentices

The time now was 1936 and although few people realised it the nation was rapidly approaching a period of great change and upheaval. The popular press had previously concentrated to a marked degree upon the latest murder trials, devoting several pages to harrowing scenes in the courtroom, reporting the evidence of Sir Bernard Spilsbury, the Home Office pathologist, for instance in great detail, dwelling on how the condemned person after enjoying a hearty breakfast, was led to the scaffold and hanged by the neck — but now more ominous news took over the headlines as the little ex-corporal from Austria led Germany on the rampage in Europe. Nor was that the only sensation to attract our attention as Edward, the uncrowned King, insisted upon pain of abdication that he would marry Wallis Simpson, an American divorcee, and make her his Queen.

The nation was divided on this issue and the topic became a constant source of conversation amongst our elders, and tempers ran high. Looking back, it is impossible to contemplate what might have happened had Edward had his way, but as youngsters of course we understood little of what was happening and cared less as we took ourselves off for a week's holiday in the Isle of Man that year. It was my first holiday without my parents and Mam worried about it. We sailed on the midnight boat from Liverpool, four of us, all apprentices. We went steerage and spent most of the night on the open deck. They sang "When my Dreamboat comes Home" with accordion accompaniment and at six in the morning we arrived at Douglas. We stayed at Cunningham's Young Men's Camp — chalet accommodation, two pounds a week with three square meals a day. It was great fun but I knew Mam wouldn't sleep thinking about us, so I sent her a couple of postcards and a box of Manx kippers to make her feel better.

After the summer break all the apprentices were moved round and I was sent to work in the Brass Finishing Shop. My first job was repairing steam gauges. Six a day you needed to repair to earn your money so you tried to get those gauges that didn't require too much attention — the others you threw at the back of a large cupboard when the chargehand wasn't looking. The trouble was that a decade of apprentices had done the same thing and one day the cupboard fell forward to reveal a huge pile of gauges which we were then made to repair. We received little or no bonus for several weeks.

As was usually the case we had one idiot with us who insisted on playing around. Vacuum gauges were tested on a column of mercury pumped to twenty-one inches and then released. The idiot thought it a good idea to pump the mercury through the top of the tube and spent the rest of the morning trying to pick it up with a magnet. The foreman wasn't very pleased especially as the same lad had recently asked him for a packet of spirit level bubbles, so he sent him home for a couple of days. Incidentally, it is interesting to note that the same boy became a comedian in later life and did quite well out of it — perhaps he wasn't such an idiot after all!

I had peeped through the massive doors of the Erecting Shop, or "Ten Shop" as it was more generally known, on more than one occasion and of course I had been taken through there as a schoolboy. Now I was to be sent to work there and I was filled with trepidation.

Imagine a building 50 feet high at its apex, some quarter of a mile long and 150 yards wide with a huge glass roof. Imagine it in summer when it resembled a huge greenhouse in whch a thousand men sweated and toiled to repair and produce some of the finest locomotives in

Erecting Shop as the author would have remembered it as an apprentice. The scene depicts the belt system.

the world. It was divided into six bays or "belts" as they were called. A-Belt for the smaller locomotives, 2-Belt for mostly Tank locomotives, B-Belt for freight and passenger locos, 4- and 5-Belt for mixed classes, and 6-Belt for New Work.

The noise was tremendous, the rat-a-tat-tat of the rivet guns, the clang of hammers on metal, the roar of the 50-ton and 25-ton cranes as they moved ponderously overhead, the hiss of acetylene torches as they burned through metal, the harsh screech of grinding wheels and the shouts of the men as they strove to make themselves heard above the din. The choking fumes from the rivet fires hung like a pall above the scene so that it was impossible to see the far end of the workshop. Whistles blew and occasionally a brass bell clanged as a signal that the locomotive, cradled like a child between the two crane hooks, was moved into the next stage of production or repair.

This then was the hell in which I found myself that Monday morning and I stood appalled at the prospect. I looked at the grey faces around me which bore witness to their years of toil, and winced that I should become part of it. But part of it I did become for I spent much of my working life in the Erecting Shop and found little romance there. Beautiful those workhorses of the railways may have been as they stood newly painted and resplendent in their livery, but they were the product of grinding toil in appalling circumstances, and I consider myself fortunate to have survived. To be fair, conditions improved dramatically through the introduction of the Health and Safety at Work Acts and now bear no comparison to those days.

I went to work with Tommy Bell — alternately nicknamed "Ding Dong" and, because he had such long legs, "Trestle Legs". Tommy helped me to adapt to the new conditions and possibly because we lived quite near to each other had a special regard for me. There was a great community spirit in those days and provided you were prepared to pull your weight you managed reasonably well.

On Christmas Eve, around two o'clock, work ceased and we enjoyed a concert with the Co-operative Band. The Head Foreman made a speech congratulating the men on their efforts during the year and for once seemed quite human. Afterwards we apprentices entered a "sticky bun" competition. The idea was that buns coated with treacle were attached to strings placed at intervals along a pole. The apprentices knelt in a row and with hands behind their backs attempted to eat the buns. Imagine the scene as the successful competitor, his face covered in treacle, then drank a bottle of pop, blew up a balloon and finally attempted to whistle! I remember my contribution was to miss the bun completely and fall flat on my face.

The following day, after the traditional Christmas dinner in the parlour, we heard the new King deliver his message to the nation.

In the New Year I received a rise; my wages were now twelve shillings plus eight shillings with additional bonus; a tradesman's wage would be about £3 per week. I started to attend night-class and I read a great deal — in this I was helped by Uncle Jack who placed his stock of books at my disposal. I often wondered what I would do after I had served my time as an apprentice but I was to be influenced by events far beyond my control.

Several of my old schoolfriends joined me in the Railway Works and I made lots of new friends. "Twitter", who I have mentioned previously, worked alongside me and he had never lost his propensity for getting into mischief. One day he and I were sent to replace a faulty steam gauge on the "Princess Elizabeth" which was standing on the test pit. We mounted the footplate of the huge locomotive beneath which several men were working and duly replaced the gauge. We savoured the moment, warming ourselves by the fire and then suddenly and without warning "Twitter" decided to touch the regulator — there was a hiss of steam and slowly the locomotive began to move, to the consternation of those working beneath it. Only the prompt action of the test pit Inspector prevented disaster as I leaped from the locomotive leaving "Twitter" petrified on the footplate. The Inspector climbed swiftly on to the footplate and slowly the loco ground to a halt several yards up the line. We both received a verbal ragging but the incident was not reported, so I suppose we were lucky.

Perhaps one of the worst jobs an apprentice had to perform was that of tank-diving. Some locomotives had huge water tanks which, like a kettle, furred with limestone which had to be scaled. The aperture through which the water entered was about eighteen inches wide so the boy selected for the tank would necessarily have to be small. He went in head-first taking with him a hammer and scaling tool together with a duck lamp — a lamp shaped like a duck's bill containing oil and a lighted wick. He needed to worm his way through the metal stays, scale the tank and replace any faulty bolts. Often there would be water in the tank so he needed to fasten his trouser bottoms with string in case the occasional frog decided to investigate.

Smoke boxes, too, were the very devil — a day's work in there and you came out covered in soot and grime which could take half the evening to remove, if you ever did. I smiled sometimes when we went to a dance at the girl in a lovely white dress embraced by some young blood out of the Erecting Shop who had spent the day in a smoke box. His hands would perspire and out would come the soot leaving large black fingerprints upon the back of her dress.

"Sniffer", one of the foremen, was heartily disliked by all and sundry. He had the nasty habit of sneaking up on you if you dared to brew a cup of tea or eat a sandwich — lunch breaks were unknown in those days, though most foremen looked the other way. "Sniffer" — hence his name — took snuff with one hand and scratched his backside with the other. We made a figure from an old pair of overalls stuffed with waste and attached a pair of worn-out shoes to them. We placed the figure behind an arc welder's screen and awaited results. They were not long in coming, "Sniffer" paused amazed at the audacity of the man apparently lying down behind a screen during working hours and kicked furiously at the boots yelling for the man to show himself. When one of the boots parted company with the overalls he realised his mistake and turned red-faced to where a crowd of grinning apprentices suddenly departed in all directions.

One thing you never had to do in the Erecting Shop was to lose your sense of humour — there was plenty to joke about despite the appalling working conditions.

There were characters too by the score, like Jimmy, sixty-four years of age, who as soon as he entered the shop in the morning did hand-stands the full length of the bays; and Sammy who regularly presented arms with a broomstick to the Head Foreman, but who nevertheless kept the bay as clean as he was able in the circumstances. Then there was Henry the charge-hand who declared war on all apprentices and threatened them regularly with "six lace-holes" or a kick up the backside if they didn't behave. There was Seth whose job it was to paint white lines down the bay: he took his job so seriously that he once painted a white line across the foreman's shiny black boots because he failed to move at the appropriate moment. But by far the funniest was Buttermilk Jack who was a little lacking "up top" — he swore he would hold the high pressure hose across his chest whilst the water was turned on. He did, and the pressure blew him across the Works yard. Undeterred and drenched to the skin, he repeated the process with the same result.

It was often said that if you could work in the Erecting Shop you could work anywhere and I think that was basically true. One thing of which I'm certain was that you learned your trade the hard way and received a second-to-none education in the school of life.

When in 1939 we prepared for our summer holidays, again in the Isle of Man, the war clouds were gathering over Europe. Air raid precaution notices were being posted and mobilisation was imminent. We hoped and prayed that it would never happen but I think we realised it was inevitable and that many of us would be called to defend our country against the tyrant as our forefathers had done. We returned home as the crisis deepened and the Nazi hordes goose-stepped through Europe, and the final treachery as they invaded Poland. The time for appeasement had passed and we must fight to defend the freedom we held so dear.

One Sunday morning I was looking out through the window as the Prime Minister, Neville Chamberlain, uttered those fateful words, declaring that we were at war with Germany. It was 11 o'clock on September 3rd, and I witnessed my first act of war as a uniformed army officer commandeered a car. That night the placards announced the sinking of S.S. Athenia and the Air Raid warning sounded for the first time in my hometown.

Conclusions

*O*n writing this book I was faced with a dilemma, not so much as to know where to commence, but rather where to finish. I have relied almost entirely on my memories of those early days and memory plays strange tricks, so I needed constantly to check my facts.

The characters have been drawn from real life though their names have been changed for obvious reasons.

I have attempted to describe what life was like in those early days against the backcloth of the socio-economic trends of that period as seen through the eyes of a young person growing up in the mid-Twenties and later in the Thirties.

Factual accounts of this period are common enough but an autobiographical account of what life was actually like in a typical railway town during the period leading up to the Second World War is a somewhat different proposition.

That the reader may form different conclusions to those I have set down is a distinct possibility and he may feel that much more might have been included. It is not possible however to include every relevant detail in so short a work, and my intention has been to give a glimpse only of what life was like in those far-off days. I have chosen to conclude with that period leading up to the Second World War for after that I feel we moved into a new era entirely, and therein lies a different story.

Les Cooper

LES COOPER

ANOTHER'S WAR

Contents

I dedicate this book to my late wife Mary
Les Cooper, 1996

*

Acknowledgements

Alan Warburton
John Mayman
Mr F Culley
Mr and Mrs A Payne
County Councillor J Minshall
Cllr P Minshall
Mr R Peel
Mr B Owen

Grateful thanks to Anne Loader

Chapter One
The Gathering Storm

Pale September sunshine slants through the narrow window panes of the tiny front parlour, and throws into stark relief the heavy furniture and the worn carpet with its Edwardian pattern. From the walls, William Ewart Gladstone, seated in a green plush armchair, gazes solemnly down, whilst in contrast on the opposite wall "Little Miss Mischief" bangs her drum and the cattle, on appropriately "An Autumn Day", meander down to the stream to drink their fill. Like miniature parachutes, tiny specks of dust drift downwards caught in a shaft of sunshine and are as suddenly gone as a passing cloud obscures the sun.

Gyp the spaniel that Dad exchanged for a racing pigeon, nuzzles the palm of my hand and makes meaningful noises punctuated by scratching at the door. From the kitchen, a clatter of dishes and muted conversation and, in the background, the radio broadcasting the traditional Sunday religious service. The Minister is asking us to pray for peace in the world, and today his words have a special significance for at 11a.m. the Prime Minister is to broadcast a special message to the nation. Our hearts are heavy for most of us have a shrewd idea of what he is likely to say.

Across the way at St. Peter's, the Morning Service has ended, and the knot of people who normally remain to converse outside the Church has dispersed. The road is silent and deserted except for the khaki-clad figure of an army officer who leans nonchalantly against a lamp post. A slight breeze dislodges a few leaves from a neighbouring tree and sends them scattering on their way like so many brown, withered, skirted creatures seeking a refuge from whatever pursues them.

Breakfast, always late on a Sunday, is long over but the scent of scorched toast still assails my nostrils and mingles with the reek of strong tobacco smoke which creeps into the room and forms little eddies which wheel and dance in the sunshine. Dad enjoys his pipe, and one could always imagine him, spectacles perched upon the end of his nose, his grizzled head buried in his newspaper whilst Mam busied herself with the household chores.

The parlour, of course, is only used for special occasions and opens on to a tiny front garden. Today, though, Mam has decided to give it an airing and a bright fire burns in the grate. As I gaze through the window the town clock competes with Christ Church to strike the hour and the clock on the mantelpiece strives to keep up with them both. The town clock wins by a whisper and is followed almost immediately by Big Ben's booming tone. A brief pause and in a voice charged with emotion the Prime Minister addresses the nation.

"An ultimatum has been sent to Germany to remove its troops from Poland or Britain would need to intervene on her behalf. No reply has been received to that ultimatum and in consequence we are at war with Germany."

The terse statement, even though I am expecting it, rings in my ears. It chills yet fascinates me. Mixed emotions surge through my body. The years of appeasement are over. My country has the courage at last to challenge the German tyrant and I might become part of that challenge. Here I am, sixteen years of age, an apprentice with the L.M.S. Railway Company: what part will I play? Will I too, like my father before me, be called to fight for my country? I feel a deep and burning hatred though of those who have contrived this war to threaten the future of millions like me, whose only desire is to sample the joys of youth and to live at peace with my neighbours.

The strains of the National Anthem have hardly died away before the officer across the way, almost as if expecting it, has commandeered a car no doubt to take him to join his Unit, and the street is deserted once again. A profound silence settles over the town such as I have never known, broken only by the hurried ticking of the clock. I turn and go into the kitchen. Dad looks up from his newspaper and gives me a quizzical glance, murmuring something about it all being over in a couple of months but his words have little conviction. Mam is pale and looks strained, I think she has been crying.

We eat our midday meal in silence and afterwards I join two friends for a stroll in the countryside.

We choose the well trodden paths past the nearby Crewe Green Church dozing in the sunshine. Down the winding lanes unsullied then by heavy traffic, past Keeper Slynn's cottage with roses fading now around the door, across the fields and over the brook running clear between its banks and on to the golf-course where we pause a while to watch the players in colourful cardigans and plus fours engrossed in their game.

Everything seems so ordinary, so peaceful. Rabbits scuttle across

Farm cottages on Lord Crewe's Estate

our path and an occasional pheasant dives for cover in the hedgerow. Smoke curls lazily from a huddle of farm cottages and the scent of burning stubble assails our nostrils. Men working in the fields look up as we pass and a single aircraft drones overhead and poses no threat — yet we are at war! As if to emphasise the fact a single cloud passes slowly across the sun and the countryside dons a shroud, discards it quickly and all is bright and cheerful once more.

Tich and I are both sixteen. Billy is going on nineteen and more worldly. Their features contrast sharply. Tich is small, hence his name. He has curly black hair and is pale faced with deep-set brown eyes. He wears a perpetual bird-like expression and bites his nails regularly. Whilst at school during biology lessons he usually fainted at the sight of blood and had to be removed from the classroom. After revival he spent the rest of the lesson reading comics in the hall. By contrast Billy is tall, well built with a shock of straw coloured hair. He has rugged features, blue eyes and a tendency to be aggressive, possibly to conceal a somewhat self conscious disposition. He smokes regularly and has nicotine stained fingers. Both he and I are employed in the railway works. Tich is apprenticed to a local butcher.

Billy clenches his cigarette between his fingers and blows smoke rings into the air. "I shall join the Navy," he announces suddenly and waits for the reaction. "See the world — that's the life!"

Tich grins but makes no comment. He obviously has in mind that on two previous occasions when we sailed to the Isle of Man, Billy had been violently sick and was known to have turned a pale shade of green when we took a rowing boat on the Park Lake.

Sensing what we were thinking Billy went on: "Of course they won't want you two, it'll all be over by the time you're eighteen."

Tich kicks the bark of a tree: "Dunno about that but if I do go it'll be the Tank Corps — always fancied driving a tank."

"Tell you what," says Billy, stubbing out his cigarette, "you'd be OK. if they dropped you behind enemy lines — you're so small they'd never notice you. How about you, Les, what do you fancy?"

"Oh, Air Force for me, if I have to make a choice," I retort .

"Brylcream boy, eh?" laughs Billy.

The conversation lapses as Billy takes out a battered copy of "Health And Efficiency", the nearest thing we ever get to porn, and thumbs through its collection of glossy photographs displaying the female form. Several oohs and ahs later he puts it away and for the rest of the afternoon we play cards stretched out beneath the oak tree.

That evening we join the crowd of youngsters on the "Rabbit Run", that being basically between the "Blue Cap Dog" and the railway bridge which spans one of the main lines. We wear our Sunday best: blue suit, white stiff collar and pointed shoes, our hair slicked back and neatly parted. The girls in two-pieces or pretty dresses glance coyly at us as we pass and we respond with a wolf whistle when some particularly attractive female goes by. Tonight though it is different. There's no friendly street lamp to light our way, or to gauge the attractiveness or otherwise of the young, or perhaps not so young, female by your side. What light there is is a mere glimmer in a sea of darkness. There is an added problem too as the gas mask slung around your shoulder repeatedly gets in the way.

The paper boys are shouting: "Special Edition, read all about it. War declared!" We buy a copy and attempt to read it by the light of a torch.

A chill wind begins to blow across the streets of my home town as suddenly the air raid siren starts to wail — and this time it is not a test, it is for real. Nothing untoward happens and the "All Clear" sounds its steady note but by that time most folk are beginning to wend their way home and the streets are rapidly becoming deserted except for the occasional drunk or a stray dog rummaging for food in some dark alley.

We wander home scarcely speaking. In a twilight world the larger shops and buildings are sharply silhouetted against the backdrop of the sky and as we cross the railway bridge a train slides to a halt outside the station belching steam and smoke which wreathes about us threatening to follow us home. The smaller shops are shuttered and dark, but here and there the terrace houses and pubs betray a glimmer of pale yellow light. The moon emerges from behind scudding clouds and bathes the street in baleful light. We shall remember this night and many more to come for this is a "Bomber's Moon".

Chapter Two
Give us this Day

I am now part of the long smoke-grimed workshops, the tall chimneys and the rows of terrace houses that surround them and stretch for the whole length of the town. Of a rookery where pigeons nest and the brown owl screeches, cheek by jowl with a score or so of shunting engines grunting and groaning as they draw the fuel and materials for the workshops.

And daily those who provide its sustenance walk, or are transported, for a twopenny fare, by the specially constructed buses with a rail down the centre to accommodate more passengers. I gaze at the newly dug gun emplacements, the air raid shelters and the barrage balloons floating over the town. The atmosphere is fogged with cigarette smoke and the faces under the peaked caps are strained, particularly amongst the older hands, but the conversation is amiable enough and morale is high. Dad sits beside me, his gas mask slung over his shoulder and his lunch box clutched beneath his arm. I gaze at him covertly, there are lines around his mouth and eyes, the long years of toil are taking their toll and this damn war doesn't help!

It's a phoney war — fighting seems remote. It's a sort of a twilight phase — the calm before the storm. There are shortages of food, sweets, petrol and rationing seems inevitable. Some try to buck the system. It's possible to sail across to Southern Ireland and return

Barrage balloons floating over Crewe. (Photo by kind permission of Mr Bernard Owen).

78

with a suitcase full of bacon, butter, meat and the like and sell it on the Black Market. The Customs are getting wise to it though and one horrible little creature who works alongside us has already been caught and fined heavily.

I've been transferred from the Machine Shop with its batteries of cream-painted lathes churning out component parts by the thousand, to the Erecting Shop, or "Ten Shop" as it is more generally known. A huge glass roofed building some quarter of a mile in length, it is capable of housing about fifty locomotives of all descriptions. It is a world smelling of metal and oil, vibrating with the noise of pneumatic rivetting. Here the huge fifty ton cranes, with smaller ones beneath them, whirr overhead, and the smoke from the rivet fires hangs like a ghastly pall over the scene. The acrid smell of electric welding is keen in my nostrils, and the harsh grating of grinding machines on metal conspires with all else to produce a cacophony of sound over which it becomes almost impossible to hear the human voice.

I am assigned to a fitter and we clamber together into the smokebox of a "Royal Scot" type locomotive. He is a huge fellow, clad in blue overalls tied with string around his ankles. He introduces himself as Jack, but is better known as "Lord Lonsdale" because he is always claiming that he once had a relationship with that gentleman. He is of florid complexion and uncertain temper and holds his head on one side. To his apprentices he is a pig and you can't expect much from a pig except a grunt! When he isn't working his main preoccupation is reading the back page of his newspaper and writing out betting slips for his apprentice to take to the bookie's runner down the bay. I was to open a slip one day and his threepence each way did not appear to indicate that he had too much faith in Lord Lonsdale as a tipster!

Jack's main sphere of expertise appears to be to fit new or repaired steam pipes to the header casting, connect them to the steam chest and replace the steam pipe packing. But the task is made more difficult by the fact that before we can do this, we must remove half a hundredweight of soot and verdigris from the smoke box floor. The soot, suitably dampened with quantities of water, is dumped into the pit below. That task accomplished and Jack is motioning me to brew the tea. During the break he sits puffing at his cigar and slurps the hot liquid down in copious draughts.

You could always tell the lads who worked in the smoke boxes because you never could completely remove the soot from your face and hands. It re-appeared when you perspired, and it caused quite a

A scene in the Smithy

giggle at the local hops when some poor devil placed his arm around a girl and left her with the imprint of his hand on the back of her pretty white dress.

Mind you, I could have fared worse, had I been smaller in stature, because I might have been selected to do "tank diving". This task had to be performed by a boy of slight stature who could manage to squeeze himself through an eighteen-inch aperture on the top of a water tank, of which there were two, one each side of that particular class of locomotive. With his overalls tied with string to prevent the odd frog from jumping up his trouser leg and armed with a pecking hammer and a duck lamp to light his way, he had to scale the tank of limestone deposits, replace the odd bolt that was leaking and seal it with red-lead. I've seen lads panic in those claustrophobic circumstances, sweat and be unable to squeeze through the aperture until they had cooled down sufficiently for them to be able to escape.

Jack has slouched off to the toilet, and I climb through the smoke-box top and perch myself on top of the boiler. The time clocks agree it is twelve noon. All the doors at the bottom of the shop are open and a draught of cold air is blowing in from the works' yard. A fussy little shunting engine is chugging up and down the line, hissing steam, its whistle blowing. The sky has an ominous yellow tinge and I think I detect the first light snowflakes. Soon it will be Christmas — the first Christmas of the War. Strange the feeling of power it gives you to gaze down from a height. Does the pilot feel like this from a much greater height? How does the bomb aimer feel when he releases his bombs? How detached — how different from the First World War and its hand-to-hand conflict fought over a few square yards of territory.

Does he feel, as he turns for home, for the awesome carnage he cre-
ates, the terrible loss in human life — innocent men, women and children, families like his own who pray for his return?

I roll a few pieces of red-lead into balls and pelt a group of pals conversing below. They reply with a barrage of wet asbestos packing. The
foreman, in blue suit and bowler hat, notes the incident and blows his
whistle sharply, then moves over to lecture the crowd below. I dive
back once more into the smoke-box.

It's difficult to remove the grime from your hands if there are no
washing facilities, but a waste patch soaked in turpentine helps.
There are rumours that washing troughs are to be installed shortly
and that a tea trolley will come round at 10a.m. and 3p.m.. They've
already had doors put on the toilets and dispensed with the services
of the lavatory clerk who took your number every time you paid a call.
Takes a war to get things moving.

I rush for my jacket and it crashes to the floor in a heap. Some
joker has filled my pockets and sleeves with steel bolts and tied them
with string. I unravel the mess and rush to the clock to join the mot-
ley throng on their way home to lunch.

My new boots are rubbing my heels and I'm limping slightly, so
I'm not sorry that I need not walk home. The sky is leaden, sleet lash-
es my face and clogs my hair, the wind shrills in the telephone wires
above my head and plays an eerie tune. I glance at the rows of newly
painted locomotives belching smoke and steam as I pass the test pits.
Passenger locos in their smart red, yellow and black livery. Two
cylinder-engines shiny black with white number plates and L.M.S. on
the side of the tenders. These are the workhorses of the railways. A
Garret with its rotary coal bunker and the new experimental Turbo
poised for a trial run. Against the skyline scores of scurrying black
matchlike figures make for the works gates and home for brief sustenance before the afternoon shift.

Dad is waiting for me in the "Spring Shop" which is part of the
huge Smithy. Here the floor is a grey dust and the furnaces, though
down for the lunch break, glow red. He is cooking eggs and bacon over
a red-hot plate and the tea is brewed in the billy can. He has a splotch
of bletch on his forehead and looks tired but he's cheerful enough as
we enjoy our lunch together. Afterwards we doze for a while and then
the buzzer is calling us back to work.

After lunch a foreman takes the new boys for a tour of the department. He's tall and paunchy with white hair that straggles beneath

his bowler hat. He has a ruddy complexion, startlingly blue eyes and a white bristling moustache. He wears a watch and chain across his waistcoat and in general appearance reminds me of Mr. Pickwick.

The workshop has six bays, two for freight, two for passenger, one for tank engines and one for the construction of new locomotives. The belt to which I have been assigned is B Belt and this is the premier Belt. The locomotives enter the shop by a traverser and after inspection are classed as casual, service or general repair. Beyond the traverser in South Shop are the vast wheel lathes, the huge planing machines and the white metalling furnaces. The locomotives are stripped and the component parts are sent to the various subsidiary workshops for repair. These include the Boiler Shop, Wheel Shop, Brass Finishing Shop, Heavy Machine Shop and Boiler Mounting Shop. The Steel Foundry, Iron Foundry and Brass Foundry provide the castings and the huge drop hammers in the Forge smash the white-hot ingots into shape at the touch of a lever or exert just enough pressure to barely crack an egg.

We gaze with awe as a forty ton loco is transported by two cranes and is lowered gently upon its wheels. I don't feel that I shall ever become used to these huge monsters passing overhead. Noise and clamour is all about me as I watch fascinated while the perspiring rivet boys hurl white hot rivets from their hearths to be caught deftly in the holder's tongs and positioned for the rivetter to hammer home with his pneumatic gun. The tour is soon over but we have learned enough of the geography of the place not to lose ourselves in the labyrinth and after the foreman has cautioned us about larking about we return to our work.

Evening has come at last and Mam is preparing our meal as we warm ourselves before the kitchen fire. The firelight glints on her smooth cheek and lush black hair streaked here and there with silver. We engage for a while in animated conversation and several kettles of hot water later emerge suitably refreshed and changed into clean clothes to join her at the table. She has more money now, what with me working and Dad getting a few nights' overtime, but the shortages are making it difficult to provide a varied meal. Queues have begun to form at many shops but the situation is faced with rough good humour and there is amongst us an immense community spirit in the face of adversity. Tonight it's rabbit stew, my favourite. I gulp it down hungrily.

I have my first real date. Pretty little thing with blonde hair, fair complexion and blue eyes, she wiggles her hips as she walks. She works for the local Council and has had a secondary school education.

I meet her on the corner by Boots the Chemist and we decide to go to the Odeon, one of the six cinemas in the town.

We sit on the back row holding hands, munching sweets. I sense her nearness and sniff the occasional whiff of her perfume. Things start to become interesting and I become oblivious to those around me and to the supporting film. The lights go up for the interval and the usherette is proffering ice cream tubs, chocolate bars and cigarettes.

After the break, "Pathe News", and the commentator tells of "The mighty German Army marching on crushing beneath its steel feet the frail bodies of the human race as it goes forward into another city to claim the bloody harvest of the battle."

It is followed by a newsreel describing the exploits of the British Expeditionary Force in France and news of the sea and air campaign against the submarine menace. Then news from the home front and the creation of a new force to combat possible invasion called "The Home Guard". News too of isolated German bombing raids on the South of England and pictures of a German bomber shot down in a field. Sports review follows and then it is time for the main film.

We sit amused at the antics of Lupino Lane in "The Lambeth Walk", and afterwards I escort the young lady home where, in a darkened doorway, her father waits to pounce upon the unsuspecting swain. I beat a hasty retreat and turn to face the darkened streets alone, and suddenly the sirens wail and searchlights stab the purple sky.

Chapter Three
The Dogs of War

"Cry havoc and let slip the dogs of war!"
Shakespeare — "Julius Caesar"

There is no Remembrance Service this year, but we go to church to pray for peace. Dad, with his four medals pinned to his breast, stands proud amongst his colleagues. In the Railway Works on Armistice Day we observe two minutes' silence and a wreath of poppies is placed on the War Memorial in the Machine Shop.

Now it's Christmas and the shopkeepers have done their best. Lights in the trees twinkle behind the shuttered windows and Father Christmas has deserted his sleigh and reindeer to arrive instead by balloon, greeted by the children waiting in Toyland. Behind many a blacked out window a fire burns cheerfully in the grate and streamers adorn the walls and brighten the dingy rooms.

Mam has somehow managed to buy a chicken, a noggin of whisky to put in our tea on Christmas morning and a cheap bottle of wine. We swap presents and after dinner the blind man from around the corner comes to entertain us with his accordion. We crack nuts and play games and Auntie Jane and Uncle Jack from next door join us for tea. Evening comes and we roast chestnuts, sing carols and choruses of "We'll Hang Out The Washing On The Siegfried Line" and "Run Rabbit Run" and Dad entertains us with a few old army songs until it is time to go to bed.

Boxing Day sees a local derby with a team from a nearby town. They're expecting 6,000 spectators and they won't be disappointed. The referee is advised to do things that only a contortionist could do and it's "Shoot, Stevens!" or maybe "Shoot the bloody lot!" They're a good humoured crowd and at half time Barry's there with his "humbugs, penny a bag, we shan't have half enough for the regulars", or there are meat pies and hot cups of tea if you're feeling the cold. Then it's home again for what's left of the Christmas dinner, a pleasant afternoon by the fireside and Christmas is over for another year.

The months pass and it is spring again. The buds are opening on the nearby trees and the streets are washed clean with April showers.

We have had our successes and the "Graf Spee" has been scuttled out-side Montevideo Harbour. Captain Langsdorf has shot himself rather than face the wrath of his Fuhrer and the crews of the "Ajax" and "Exeter" have covered themselves with glory.

On the home front sporadic air attacks on south coast airfields and installations have been repulsed and the enemy, it is said, have suf-fered heavy losses. We have a National Government now, led by Winston Churchill, in which all political parties serve. The King and Queen have visited our town and talked to the men in the factories, particularly the newly opened "Rolls-Royce" which is now in full pro-duction making aero engines. The streets are lined with people but not a single worker leaves his post. They talk, too, to the air raid war-dens, the auxiliary firemen, the ambulance men and the newly emerging Civil Defence workers in their distinctive green uniforms upon whom the safety of the town and its people now depends.

How strange that in time of war people from so many different backgrounds and political beliefs can merge together to fight the com-mon enemy, and yet in peace time seek only self interest and sow dis-cord amongst their fellow men. If only the energy generated in war could be harnessed in peace to serve the common good: what goals we could achieve, what happiness could be ours! "Away with tawdry peace" says a First World War poet. "Clean like a swimmer into water" we must face the challenge of war. But he did not leave these shores and never slept in Flanders' Fields.

And as the grey-clad jack-booted hordes sweep across Norway gaining control over the Baltic and overwhelming the Low Countries so that at last they stand poised at the gates of Paris itself, which has been declared a free city. The refugees stream across the Channel under the umbrella of Allied air and sea power, and the battered rem-nants of the British Expeditionary Forces turn to face the tyrant at Dunkirk. The epic withdrawal from Dunkirk will live forever in the pages of history and will be hailed, not as a defeat, but as a victory in the face of tremendous odds. The fact that so many have survived to reach their homeland is due entirely to the awesome courage of those who fought to rescue them from the jaws of death by any form of transportation available at their command. Young and old, each play a part. Many are lost but for their sacrifice thousands are saved and return to fight another day.

At the Theatre, as part of a programme designed to boost our morale, a French refugee sings of the love of his country and concludes with "And to hell with Burgundy": "Germany" is substituted for "Burgundy", and with tears streaming down his face he leaves the stage and the entire audience stands to applaud him.

You can buy a radio now with short wave for three shillings a week and listen to that arch comedian of German broadcasting in English, Lord Haw-Haw. In sneering nasal tones he relates a whole string of German victories at sea and in the air and predicts that Hitler himself will soon be here to treat with Winston Churchill in London. Churchill himself addresses the nation and tells us that we alone now of all the European nations stand against the might of the German Empire and promises naught but "blood, sweat and tears" in the months to come.

The siren wails frequently now and the sound of anti-aircraft fire is heard nearby. A bomb explodes in a field outside the town which kills two cows and injures a farm hand on his way to work.

The Government has realised the importance of rail communications and the factories are now almost wholly turned over to war production. The workshops themselves have their own system of air raid precautions and an identity card is issued to each member of staff. Air raid shelters are dug and a warning light system is installed. Yellow for approaching aircraft, purple for those in the immediate vicinity and red for directly overhead. More staff have been recruited and there's talk of employing female workers. Those who left the rail service to join the Forces have been sent back, but some sadly will not return. Railway employees are now deemed to be in a reserved occupation and will not be called to join the Forces. Nevertheless all persons must carry a national registration card and my age group has already been called to submit to a medical examination and be registered for military service. I have received grade AI and am not displeased by that. A section of the workshop is screened and is to be known as Z shop. This will be utilised for tank production and specialist workers have been allocated to key positions.

I work now with Albert, a tall gaunt individual with watery blue eyes and a stern expression. He is a local preacher and has strictly moral ideas of how one should behave. I play along having once been a pupil at his Sunday School. He asks me to "ascertain" the time and enquires whether his collar is dirty in which case he will have to "discard" it! I am glad to have escaped working with Alec though, who occasionally places his arm around you and calls you "dear" as he tentatively touches your backside.

The Boiler Shop at Crewe LMS Works

At lunch break, Albert sits beside me eating sparingly and reading his Bible or perhaps a copy of "Methodist Weekly". Occasionally he quotes a passage to me and lectures to me gently on patterns of behaviour. I respond respectfully and our relationship with each other blossoms. Until one day, I miss my aim with the hammer and hit my thumb nail instead. I react with a spate of expletives and Albert loses faith in human nature and fails to communicate for a couple of days. Not unsurprisingly I am then sent to work with "Ding Dong" who insists his apprentices call him Mr. Bell. Mr. Bell lives quite near to me and has known me since I was a boy. The work is hard, but he is a fair man, we form a lasting friendship and he teaches me much about workshop practice. Sadly he was later killed along with his wife in an air raid, but that is another story.

By the time I'm almost eighteen I've joined the Union for sixpence a fortnight, am doing an N.C.L.C. course in English, attending technical school one night week, have been rostered for firewatching for both the town and the Railway Company and for good measure have joined the Labour Party. I have also been enlisted in the Rescue Service of the Civil Defence Corps. Apart from that my time is my own, which virtually mounts to one half a day a week on a Saturday with perhaps an occasional Sunday.

Firewatching, now there's a thing! You book on at eight o'clock in the evening assuming you've finished work by then and proceed to any one of several huts dotted around the works perimeter. Inside the huts, which are almost always filthy and poorly lit, there are several bunks with a couple of blankets. There is a table and chairs and a few pegs on the wall upon which to hang your coat. There you await the arrival of the fire officer who details your duties.

"In the event of a raid your position will be at this point," and he acquaints you with the various fire fighting appliances within the area. After that he wishes you a pleasant evening and departs forthwith.

It is really not funny to realise that you are standing within a few feet of oil and grease installations containing several hundred barrels of the stuff and that an incendiary bomb might descend upon them at any time. It's doubtful that you would have time to connect up any fire fighting equipment even if you could find it in the stygian darkness. The only possible consolation could be that your departure from this world would be accelerated to a considerable degree. In addition to the obvious hazards there is the problem of the bed bugs who insist upon sharing your lodging with you. In order to avoid their attentions you sit at the table most of the night and play cards or read a book. In the morning you are paid the statutory three shillings and after breakfast return to work.

On such a morning I am standing on a bridge spanning the railway lines near to the hut where I have spent the night. It is 6a.m. and the sky is streaked with a pink dawn. The birds in chorus greet the new day and the cold air brushes my cheek. From out of the distance a black shape appears travelling amazingly fast towards me, perhaps fifty feet above the ground. It streaks above my head, barely clearing the bridge and the brown helmeted figure in the cockpit glares through his goggles at me as he zooms away. The siren starts to screech a warning but it is too late as two loud explosions threaten to burst my eardrums and two columns of smoke arise into the air above the workshops barely a quarter of a mile away. Disturbed the birds chatter noisily and from somewhere a dog howls twice and then is silent.

Chapter Four
Troglodytes

And now the night sky is made hideous with the blood-red glow of a thousand fires. The raiders return day and night from their bases in France to bomb and lay waste our proud Northern cities. The explosions are plainly audible for miles around and the searchlights criss-cross the night sky seeking a target. The guns fire and anti-aircraft shells burst above our heads. We are becoming a nation of troglodytes spending much of our time in air-raid shelters deep underground. Once there we sit on the wooden benches with our feet dangling in water. Some sit stolidly gazing at the dirt walls hardly bothering to speak, whilst others at the first sound of gunfire attempt to bury themselves within them.

Mam refuses to go to the shelters now and sits for long hours beneath the stairs. We have barely eaten our evening meal when the siren shrieks its warnings. I stand at the front door and look up at the darkening sky. I hear the sound of approaching aircraft — throbbing unsynchronised engines — and know that they are German. Seventeen in vee formation pass overhead on their way to bomb Liverpool. Anti-aircraft shells burst beside the leading plane and are followed almost immediately by the whistle of a descending bomb. A loud explosion and plumes of smoke rise above the town. Shock waves reverberate amongst the buildings and hurl me gasping against the wall. The word "troglodyte" begins to take on a new meaning. Some prefer the Anderson shelter in the back garden to the often claustrophobic conditions in the public shelters but in either case it means long periods underground. Each evening the planes pass noisily overhead. The guns fire and the exploding shells rip open the night sky punctuated by the scream of a descending bomb. The whole town shakes and the clamour of fire engines on their way to deal with fires caused by incendiary bombs adds to the confusion. A flare is dropped floating down on a parachute illuminating the whole town so that it is possible to read a newspaper in its baleful glare.

In daylight battles rage above our heads for the conquest of the skies and the sharp crackle of machine gun fire echoes in our ears. Tiny vapour trails betray the aircrafts' presence and fade to form myriad patterns in the sky.

Night and day work in the factories is constantly interrupted as the red light flashes and we are herded to the shelters to huddle together until the danger has passed.

In London and the larger cities the situation is far more serious. The underground stations have become a haven for thousands, many homeless, who have taken up residence there bringing with them all they possess. Children are evacuated into the countryside to find refuge in small towns and villages throughout the land. Many have drunk milk but have never seen a cow. They enjoy, perhaps for the first time, a totally different lifestyle.

An entirely new word has entered the English language — it is 'Coventrate" — as that fair city is razed to the ground with hundreds of its citizens entombed within the air raid shelters. There remains little of the beautiful cathedral that dominated the city and its ruined tower is all that is left to remind future generations of the futility of war.

Against this background many of my family and friends have become dispersed. Dora, my cousin from next door, has joined the A.T.S. and is stationed at Chislehurst, a far cry indeed from her years of "service" at Alderley Edge. Harry her brother, a Territorial, is at an Army base in Derby. Tich has given a false age and has joined a tank regiment and I have lost touch with Billy altogether.

To compensate perhaps I have made a host of new friends.

I'm over eighteen now and sneak an occasional drink with Dad at the local. Basically the pub is divided into three separate rooms. The

The Lord Nelson - a Wilson's house frequented by the author as a young man

parlour for mixed company, the first bar which is patronised almost entirely by the pigeon flying community and the second devoted to darts and dominoes. Because of his interest in pigeon flying Dad frequents the first bar. Here the conversation when not discussing the war revolves around football, boxing, and horse racing but much more frequently the techniques that need to be employed in order to ensure that your particular bird arrives home at the cote before all others.

In the event of an air raid the customers retire to the cellar taking their liquid refreshment with them to continue their discussion there and the landlord provides a few sandwiches in case their stay is prolonged.

There has been the odd occasion when things have become hectic and they have left their pint pots on the bar only to have found them drained when they have returned. But this is an exception rather than the rule.

Bob, a friend of Dad's, says the only thing to do is to "keep on jogging along". When the windows shatter from the blast and chaos is all around he puffs his foul smelling pipe in indignation or gulps down his pint of bitter with a frown. The only sign of concern is that his knuckles have whitened somewhat as they clutch the edge of the bar.

Occasionally we visit the cinema or the Lyceum Theatre. It's mostly at weekends for there's little opportunity during the week. It's a risky business for the show is often interrupted by air raid warnings flashed up on the screen or announced from the stage: "You are advised that you remain at your own risk." It's a bit disconcerting when the film is quivering to the sound of gun fire or the comedian is looking anxiously towards the exit.

We return home through the darkened streets and we encounter a further hazard in the shape of a dozen smoke screen canisters. These canisters are about four feet high and puff out clouds of evil-smelling smoke that gets into your eyes and makes you cough. It is an attempt to confuse the raiders and in that it may be successful but to walk into one of these drunk or sober is not an experience to be relished.

It has been decided that I do a spell of night work at the factory and I am warned that the experience is unlikely to give me pleasure.

The Erecting Shop is completely blacked out and one must enter by a series of tunnels to emerge in a dimly lit interior. It has at night a cave-like aspect and what little light there is silhouettes the locomotives standing in rigid lines down their separate bays. The reddish glow from the rivet fires provides a suffused illumination of its own. The only real light is from the electric cable lamps slug from the locomotives but even they are shaded. The general impression would be of a descent into the underworld and the shadowy figures there its denizens.

Masses of material lie between the bays. Boilers, fire boxes, wheels and a hundred different component parts. Should the red light flash you must negotiate this mass of materials and arrive by the best way possible at the exit points. It is the group leader's task to ensure the safety of his group and lead them to the shelters.

Of course, considering the risks involved to life and limb of facing these hazards, some prefer to remain where they are and hope that the place will not receive a direct hit.

The fitter with whom I have been chosen to work is a known character. He is a drinking man and of uncertain temper. He has been known, I'm told, to reduce his apprentices to tears. It is rumoured that he has a silver tube in his stomach which it appears does little to improve his temper.

He discovers me eventually and his "Hey you, come with me" does nothing to reassure me.

The days that follow are sheer hell. He curses me at every opportunity, throws things at me and casts doubt upon my parentage. I strive to do his bidding and attempt to reason with him, but it is to no avail. I arrive home physically and mentally exhausted and collapse on my bed. I dread the night approaching. I cannot sleep and I cannot eat properly because of the unnatural hours. Towards the end of the second week I snap and my thoughts are only of vengeance.

I am squatting on a locomotive frame some two feet above his head and I'm striving to complete a task he has assigned to me. His bald head glints in the pale light of the hand lamps, he is perspiring and cursing softly to himself as he attempts to ram home a stubborn bolt. I dangle the two pounds hammer above his head and it slips from my grasp and lands firmly on the back of his head. A tiny trickle of blood stains his collar.

His face is purple as howling with pain he leaps from beneath the locomotive.

"Did you do that on purpose?" he growls and curses me horribly.

"Of course not, quite accidentally," I retort calmly. "Just like you've tried to cripple me for the last fortnight and I'll tell you this — the next time it'll not be a two pounds hammer, it will be a seven pounds one and you won't get up again!"

His face is livid. He tries to speak but can't. Instead he rushes to the nearest ambulance box to obtain treatment .

I'm on the mat before the night foreman. He asks for an explanation and I state my case. He remonstrates a little but I sense a sympathetic ear and I am sent to work elsewhere with a promise that I shall be returned to the day shift the following week.

It's 3a.m. on the second part of my shift. The klaxon shrieks and the red light flashes. Above the din there is the sound of approaching

An evening scene during the blackout: from "LMS at War"

aircraft and the guns are firing. The place is in utter darkness within seconds and I flick my torch to light my way to the exits. All is confusion and a man is screaming for help. He's jammed fast between the slide bars of a four foot three locomotive. He's fat and the more he struggles the less chance he has of escaping. He's groaning now but we can't locate him in the darkness and will have to leave him there. Nearby a man dives into the firebox of a locomotive for shelter only to find that it has no ash pan and he crashes through into the pit. He lies there gasping and I shout for help but no one hears. So I make him as comfortable as possible on some old sacking.

We cross the bridge over the railway line and plunge into the shelters. It seems ages before the man who was trapped staggers into join us, his clothes ripped to shreds. There are streaks of blood on his face and in his hair. His arm is hanging limply by his side. I think it is broken. An ambulance man brushes past to attend to his injuries.

In the darkness, someone puffs a cigarette: it glows red for a while and then is extinguished.

After what seems an eternity the "All Clear" sounds and we struggle back to the workshops.

The man who leapt into the firebox has a broken leg and is suffering from concussion. He is lifted gently onto a stretcher and the ambulance moves slowly away. For the record: *no damage has been reported and two men have been slightly injured...*

Chapter Five
For Those We Loved

*I*t's a decent enough little town, typical of many in the North except here the railways are dominant and other industries a poor second, up till the coming of Rolls-Royce, of course, which now provides employment second only to the railways.

It has one of the largest stations in Britain and has massive marshalling yards at Basford Hall. It has suffered dreadfully from the Depression years and the scars are there to see, but it has fine Municipal Buildings and a large Town Hall in which dances and numerous functions take place. It has an excellent park too donated to it by the fathers of the railways, and a large market which is held on Fridays, Saturdays and Monday mornings.

This is a quiet neighbourhood quite close to the town but not too far from the countryside to prevent us from enjoying its attractions. It has a fine parish church, that of St. Peter's, and its main street boasts eight public houses and a hotel. Jutting out from the main street, which is a hive of small shops catering for most needs, there are numerous side streets and alleys and rows of small mean terraced dwellinghouses. Though mean in appearance the doors benefit from the occasional lick of paint, usually green or brown and the steps are kept clean with a rub of the donkey stone. Nearby the Crosville Bus

Streets of terraced homes housed the railway workers

Company has its depot built in 1926 which occasionally causes some aggravation to those living in close proximity.

The people are mostly artisans, tradesmen or shopkeepers with a sprinkling in the better areas of a few school teachers, office workers, and at least one doctor. Most worship at the same church or chapel and are steadfast in their beliefs, at least on Sundays. Most people know each other or are on nodding terms. There is a tremendous community spirit and neighbours frequently drop in to converse or borrow the odd cup of sugar. Doors are usually open for there is no fear of intrusion especially in the daylight hours. They have little enough to share but what they have they share willingly with the less fortunate.

From such a background, I form a deep and, I think, lasting friendship with Arthur who lives quite near and whose father works with my own in the Smithy.

He is pale, short of stature but with bright brown eyes set in oval features and has black wavy hair. He is a great favourite with the girls who constantly vie for his attention. I frequently have to settle for second best, but bear no resentment. Over the next few months we become like brothers, going everywhere together. I am grateful for his friendship, particularly now that I have been transferred to the older part of the works and am employed along with Arthur in the "Stay Shop" turning out boiler stays for the locos.

The work is less arduous and I am much nearer to home so that we walk to work together. I do miss the comradeship though of many of the friends I have left behind in the Erecting Shop, and even have less malice for those who persecuted me.

Dad has left for work and I am finishing my breakfast, when suddenly and without warning, two loud explosions rend the air. The whole house shakes and the bread that Mam is cutting jumps from the table. Pictures leap from the walls and crockery slides from the table to smash itself upon the tiled floor. I rush to the door and a woman from across the way is screaming hysterically that she's seen his bloody wheels drop off. I gaze skyward and see the JU88 wheeling and diving to avoid the barrage balloons over the town. A sharp crackle of machine gun fire and one balloon disintegrates in flames above me and nosedives to the ground a blazing mass. From the direction of the old works two huge columns of smoke are rising into the morning air. The clangour of the fire bells is not long delayed and too late the siren shrieks its warning.

We reach the works to find utter confusion. Part of the old Smithy has been hit and the Tin Shop and Plating Shop destroyed. The Stay Shop has received minor damage but no work can take place as the power lines are down. There are some casualties but they are not so heavy as expected. The night staff file through the gates ghostly pale covered in grey dust so that you can barely discern their features. The ambulance teams rush to attend them and the women from the near-by houses hurry to provide hot tea and whatever comfort they can give. Arthur is beside me and there are tears in his eyes as we wend our way home together.

I'm working Sundays now and several nights overtime so that I avoid being rostered for fire watching. One night each week I engage in rescue service training at the Secondary School. I have been given a smart black uniform with yellow flashes on the collar and a black beret with the insignia R.S. woven into it.

Tubby, our instructor, asks for a volunteer to act as a casualty to be swung on a stretcher from the roof of the building. No one steps forward so he selects one — a tall gangling youth roughly clad and slow of speech, he comes from a neighbouring village.

He hesitates. "Not with you buggers tying the knots I'm not!" he protests. Eventually, he is persuaded on condition that Tubby inspects the knots and the exercise proceeds as planned.

I am not to know it, but soon my training will be put to the test.

Towards the end of this year we have inflicted tremendous casualties on the enemy in the skies above Britain. Daylight raids have become sporadic but the nightly bombing of our towns and cities, particularly in the southern half of Britain, continues unabated. Hitler has declared total war upon his enemies and Mussolini, his Axis partner, has come to his aid.

The newsreels and radio broadcasts tell us of the enormous courage of our seamen who against all odds strive to keep the sea lanes open for our shipping. Of the tremendous courage of our merchantmen who like the "Jervis Bay" fought to the last gasp against the formidable power of the "Admiral Scheer" in order to protect the rest of the convoy.

Nevertheless, the submarine menace increases and the enemy are now sowing magnetic mines and strafing our shipping in the channel in an attempt to starve us into submission.

Daily news bulletins tell us of successes in the desert campaign where our army under Wavell has captured Sidi Barrani and halted the Italian advance.

An air raid warden scans the skies : from "LMS at war."

In Europe the Russian Bear has invaded Poland and Finland and thus sealed her back door against her former treaty partners. The signs are ominous perhaps, as the tyrant rampages through the rest of Europe, that he may turn his eyes towards her and the tremendous resources she could provide to aid the German War Machine.

Nightly now our bombers are carrying out raids upon German towns and cities and as we sit crouched each night in the shelters we have at least the consolation that the enemy is also suffering as we have done during the last year.

In my home town damage has been relatively slight and casualties few. After the Battle of Britain we have relaxed our vigilance somewhat and perhaps become complacent particularly during daylight hours.

Realising though the importance of rail communications the Germans have resorted to bombing raids upon railway workshops and marshalling yards and considerable damage has been inflicted on such installations in many parts of the country. Some such raids have been carried out by comparatively few planes, sometimes a single aircraft, perhaps a Heinkel or JU88.

Sunday afternoon and nearing the end of the shift, we are loading a steel bar into an ancient lathe at the far end of the workshop. The belts and pulleys above our heads are groaning a protest at the increased effort demanded of them and the die boxes screech as they

The Rolls-Royce factory suffered a direct hit.

thread the copper boiler stays. The labourer is loading swarf from the lathes into his barrow — he smiles as we pass. Everything is normal — so utterly normal. Suddenly there are two deep thuds and the whole department rocks. We are showered with pieces of wood and splinters as we race wildly for the exit. There is no time to go to the shelters so we dive, two of us together, beneath a ballast wagon on the railway track. We see the plane on its wing tips no more than twenty feet above the track rushing towards us cannon shelling the line as it streaks across the works yards. Men are diving for cover and are scattered like nine pins. The plane turns, repeats the performance and then as quickly is gone. We struggle, half scared out of our wits, from beneath the ballast wagon and look up to see a huge pall of smoke rising above the nearby Rolls-Royce factory. It has been a direct hit and we know the casualties will be heavy.

That evening our worst fears are confirmed. The bombs have hit No. 16 Shop, sixteen are dead and more than sixty injured. Twiddling with the radio knobs I hear Lord Haw-Haw's gloating tones as he relates the incident. I feel I could strangle him. This is my town and these are my people.

Chapter Six
Arthur

On occasional break from duty we find time to stroll in Queen's Park. It is Autumn and the trees are shedding their leaves to form a pattern of red and gold along the avenue leading to the South African War Memorial and the black and white pavilion. The soldier gazes down upon the scene, standing rigidly to attention, his rifle by his side. Below him and on each side of the monument the plaques contain the names of those who fell in battle.

Arthur kicks at the fallen leaves. He is very pale and seems ill at ease. He has failed his medical examination and has been graded "F", unfit for military service. Despite this he has joined the Home Guard. He has a racking cough and Mam thinks he may be suffering from T.B..

Pale sunshine penetrates the mist over the lake and the slight breeze makes brave attempts to disperse it. The few people around have gathered in the Pavilion drinking watery tea or perhaps a mug of Bovril.

"A short life and a gay one," says Arthur smiling wanly over the rim of his cup.

"Though now it's not so gay, is it?"

I try hard to console him and tell a few jokes.

A young couple in the corner appreciate the jokes and she giggles uncontrollably whilst he looks uncomfortable.

We stroll together through the almost deserted streets, have a shandy at the local and then go home for lunch and a slice of the joint that seems to diminish in size each passing week.

It's amazing though that in times of shortages how inventive the average housewife can become. Nothing is wasted and what we have is served in a dozen different ways. The small Sunday joint is served hot or cold with a few lettuce leaves and half a tomato and the remainder in soup with a few vegetables. You can buy a rabbit for a few pence and make a pie or a nourishing stew. Threepenny worth of meat and potato pie from the local shop with a jug of gravy provides a meal for two or even three if you add a few more vegetables. An egg fried with a slim rasher of bacon provides your breakfast or when the bacon has gone, the egg scrambled, poached or boiled with a round of toast. You can buy dried eggs too which served in different ways are quite palatable. Fish has become a staple diet but it is shortly to become scarce as the fishing grounds have become limited because of the ever-growing submarine menace around our shores. Fresh fruit is available, apples, pears and the like, and home grown vegetables, but exotic fruit from abroad such as bananas and oranges are difficult to obtain and are sometimes auctioned to the highest bidder at some charity fair. We are relying now far more upon our own resources for food and there is talk of forming a Land Army to provide and co-ordinate our food supplies.

Much of the clothing industry has been switched to providing uniforms and there is little choice in the shops of the more stylish apparel. Clothes have become more austere in design and for us youngsters a sports coat and grey flannel trousers in Summer, and in Winter a suit, blue serge or the like and an overcoat, blue or grey, with a white scarf becomes the vogue. Here again the average housewife with a sewing machine or perhaps by hand produces her own creations from a remnant bought from behind the Market and amazes us with a real inventiveness in colour and design. Footwear too becomes a problem, especially leather, and the cobbler's shop receives extra patronage.

Entertainment has now become an important element in our lives, particularly as it is almost always designed to boost morale. Most shows are twice-nightly and provide an opportunity for those working long hours in the factories to enjoy a late performance. In cinemas the main feature film is often supported by a newsreel and a propaganda film. The Lyceum Theatre provides twice-nightly variety performances, a play or perhaps a Gilbert and Sullivan opera — "H.M.S. Pinafore", "The Pirates of Penzance" or "The Mikado" produced by the local "Old Studs".

Arthur and I often attend such shows sitting in the gallery or "Gods" as it is known for the price of a fourpenny ticket and pelting the audience in the huge auditorium below with screwed up pieces of toffee paper or orange peel before that fruit became in short supply.

Tonight we are going to see Charles Laughton in "Jamaica Inn" at the "Empire". I've read the book and am looking forward to seeing the film.

There is a touch of frost in the air and we turn up the collars of our overcoats against the chill. The moon rides high in the sky and there are a few scudding clouds about which but briefly obscure it from view. It is a typical bomber's moon.

Several times during the performance air raid warnings flash up on the screen but are as quickly followed by the "All Clear" so that we keep our seats and enjoy the show.

Afterwards we walk home and have little difficulty in avoiding the smoke screens puffing brown evil smelling vapours into the air for they are brilliantly illuminated in the light of a full moon. We pause for a while to chat outside my home when suddenly the air raid siren shrieks its warning and dark figures appear as if from nowhere scurrying to the shelters. Jackie Paper's clogs can be heard clattering across the pavement — he is always first in the shelters and just as surely will be the last to depart. We say goodnight with a cheery "see you in the morning" and go our separate ways.

Just after 10.30p.m. the bombs explode in a quarter circle damaging the railway line and setting fire to the station. All the shops across the way have their windows smashed by the blast and several incendiary bombs are blazing on the roofs of buildings nearby. Confusion reigns as the N.F.S. deals with the fires and the ambulances with casualties which fortunately are light. Noise and confusion dies away to be replaced by a deep abiding silence which lasts for several hours but no "All Clear" is sounded.

Dad has gone to bed tired out after his day's work and the fire is low in the grate. Mam stares steadfastly into space, she will not rest until the "All Clear" has sounded. Dad's best suit, damp after a recent

Shops in Earle Street badly damaged by the bombing in 1941. (Picture loaned by J J Minshall, Curator, Cheshire Constabulary Museum).

Bomb damage in Earle Street, 1941. (Picture loaned by J J Minshall, Curator, Cheshire Constabulary Museum).

shower, is airing by the fireside.

My eyes are all but closing as I lounge in the armchair. I ask if Mam minds if I go to bed for a couple of hours. She demurs but finally accepts that I need my rest.

I fall asleep almost immediately and suddenly there's the scream of a diving plane, red flashes, tremendous bangs and then blackness. Like emerging from an anaesthetic, stark reality asserts itself and I am lying on the floor beside my bed with part of the window frame draped around my neck.

Mam is screaming and gabbling incoherently about Dad's suit being covered in soot. Dad is up in a flash and it is obvious to us that part of the house has disappeared. There are gaping holes in the walls and beams at a crazy angle block our way. We manage to get outside. The street is a blazing ruin — several gas mains have exploded and the church across the way is illuminated in a strange unearthly glow. The cross is lying in the middle of the road and I wonder at how large it is for I have never seen it this way. In the back garden lies a cross beam from one of the houses and on the clothes line are draped a dozen articles of clothing. Money is scattered all around and the pitiful chattels from a dozen houses are strewn in wild confusion about the garden. Overhead the plane carrying the author of destruction still lurks, gratified perhaps that he has struck a blow for the Fatherland.

More devastation greets us as we go into the street. A whole row of houses has all but disappeared and many more are seriously damaged and on fire. The pilot can only have believed that the bus garage was a railway installation and that being adjacent to the railway bridge and station was in fact a legitimate target. The only alternative is to conclude that the bombing is quite indiscriminate.

I volunteer to help with what little skill I have and am eagerly accepted. The screams of the wounded and the dying are indescribably terrible as we struggle to rescue people from the blazing inferno. One woman is trapped by a beam with her backside in the fire. We remove the beam and she is taken horribly burned and unconscious to the waiting ambulances. A dog is similarly trapped and is whining pitifully. We remove the obstruction and the animal leaps forward to crash down again dead at our feet. These are my neighbours and I know them all. The newsagent, dying of cancer, but now relieved of his torment. The builder with his wife and pretty daughter who lie together in the debris with hardly a mark upon them, killed by blast.

Bomb damage in Earle Street, 1941. (Picture loaned by J J Minshall, Curator, Cheshire Constabulary Museum).

Bomb damage in Earle Street, 1941. (Picture loaned by J J Minshall, Curator, Cheshire Constabulary Museum).

Some are saved to relive the memories of that terrible night — to survive, as I will, to jump at the sound of a motor cycle's backfire and live again in memory this dreadful night. Bravery there is around me and cowardice too as some would bury themselves within the walls of the shelters rather than lift a finger to help.

Morning comes at last and in the dawn we are better able to see the awful desolation all around. The smoke rises from the fires now quenched but with here and there a flicker from the gas mains. Some dozen houses have been completely destroyed and others badly damaged. Two craters have appeared in the park where I played as a child and the church steeple lolls at a crazy angle. By the railway bridge a time bomb rests against one of the pillars and I'm told children are hitting it with a hammer. We send for the bomb squad to defuse it.

Three of us are sitting by the lamp standard in the middle of the road and we share a cigarette, a "Tenner Brand" between us. An ambulance man asks whether we are OK and we reply in the affirmative. He asks me to stand and my legs turn to jelly. I drop my trousers and he injects a sedative. I feel woozy and am taken by ambulance to the hospital. Two hours and several cups of tea later I am back home again. The windows are shattered, most of the slates are missing and part of one wall has collapsed — but it is still my home and thank God my family are there to greet me.

Later I am told that Arthur has been killed. I am numb with shock, hardly able to comprehend the awful truth.

It seems that after leaving me he went home and after the first bombs fell went out to visit a colleague.

On the way home he picked up a fragment of a bomb, or perhaps a piece of shrapnel, and showed it to his father. Clearly imprinted there were the letters A.C. — by some stroke of fate his initials. His father warned him not to go out again but he did so and when the second stick of bombs fell he ran with a friend into an uncompleted shelter. The shelter received a direct hit.

I attend the funeral of the victims, all seventeen of them, including Arthur, and a school friend plays the "Last Post" over Arthur's grave. One day I will pluck up enough courage to ask Arthur's father whether they ever found him and, if not, what I wonder did we carry into the church that day?

Chapter Seven
The Way we Were

*I*t's a grey November day. The mist is dispersing slowly to give way to a pale watery sun. The trees, such as they are in the town centre, have all but lost their leaves and they lie brown and sodden upon the pavements. Still at a distance, the strains of military music, the deep beating of the drums, mingles with the strident notes of the trumpets and the thud of marching feet.

We gaze fixedly at the memorial to the dead of the First World War and wonder. I glance at the small khaki-clad group of the Home Guard standing rigidly to attention and pick out the gaunt figure of my father with his medals pinned to his breast. I am proud, but so sad that it has come to this. I wonder what he is thinking. He that was promised a country fit for heroes to live in and came home to suffer the worst effects of the Depression and several years' unemployment during which time I was born. Shall we ever learn, I wonder?

All around me now the massed ranks of the armed services in their uniforms of sombre hue. In response to the shouted command their boots ring against the paving stones and their rifles snap smartly into place. Here and there a splash of colour — the Civil Defence, men and women in their smart green uniforms, the auxiliary fire service in blue with red flashes, white helmeted A.R.P. wardens, the police force, ambulance service, white satchels slung around the shoulders, Red Cross nurses, men and women of the British Legion and representatives from a dozen different auxiliary units including the Rescue Service in which I myself serve.

One section only now remains to be filled. Led by the top-hatted figure of the Mayor's attendant, the Town Clerk appears, accompanied by the Mayor in scarlet robes, followed by the Minister of Christ Church and, to bring up the rear, the serving members of the Town Council.

A short service at the cenotaph and then the band leads us on to Church Parade. This year we have paid tribute to those who fell in the first World War and now we pray for a swift end to this one. Hypocrisy, the cynic may well argue, especially as so many of our people are today paying the ultimate sacrifice in a war that is not of their making. From the depth of our despair, hope springs eternal that we the new generation shall play our part in creating a new society free from the threat of war and that our suffering shall not have been in vain.

Young though I am I am beginning to feel that the attitude to this war is entirely different from that in the First World War. There is little or no jingoism, far more community spirit in the face of adversity and a steadfast desire to rid the world of tyranny is manifest in all we are trying to achieve. I feel that after this war is over people will no longer be prepared to accept the mass unemployment, poor working conditions and large scale deprivation of the masses as our forefathers did, and will create a new and far more equal society in which our people can live and enjoy the fruits of their labours. It's an optimistic concept considering the nature of mankind perhaps, but one I feel which can, and must, be achieved.

We are approaching the second Christmas of the war.

Behind the glitter, shortages are becoming acute. The housewife needs to become even more inventive as more food and goods are rationed. Soap is rationed, sugar and fats are in very short supply and there is talk of clothes rationing. Cigarettes are regionalised and it has become impossible to obtain certain brands.

I'm taking a drink regularly now and the cheery atmosphere and social intercourse helps to boost morale somewhat. Surprising what a couple of glasses of best bitter and a jolly old sing-song around the "joanna" can do for a body. The public bar is seen as an island of refuge in a sea of darkness.

Mam didn't like it when I started smoking, said that if people were meant to smoke they would have a chimney on their heads. She likes my drinking even less. It's very rare that she will take a drink in a public house but she enjoys a glass of port at home around Christmas time and sometimes a spot of whisky in her tea — for medicinal purposes, of course! Dad on the other hand enjoys his pint, he needs it after all with the sort of heavy job he has to do.

"Chuckles", so called because he never smiles, is describing an air raid but unfortunately he suffers from an unfortunate tendency to malapropism. "I tell yer I saw 'em," he says. "There they were coming over in formentations of three and then the handicraft guns opened up. Making a 'ell of a mess of Random aren't they?" he goes on. "They're always dropping bombs there — I can't understand it!"

Walter peers at him over the rim of his pint pot and then nudges my elbow. "Thick as two short planks," he says. "Silly bugger — can't tell his backside from his elbow."

Two French sailors are engaged in animated conversation at the far end of the bar whilst at the serving hatch a young Polish soldier is trying to make himself understood in halting English. He's asking for schnapps but we don't have any. These three are typical of many nationalities, uniformed as well as civilian, who managed to escape from Europe before it was too late. Soldiers, sailors and airmen have now joined the free forces in this country planning, fighting and working for the day when they can return to their own lands.

Above the rattle of dominoes and the slap of darts upon the board together with the general babble of voices Dad is trying to make himself heard.

"Down the old sunken road I was, middle of the night, pitch black on sentry duty. Somewhere near Poperhinge I think we were. Guns firing in the distance, you could hear the rumble and see the flashes — like lightning it was !" He takes a gulp of his beer.

"Comes on to rain a bit and I'm trudging back and forth across a patch of muddy ground with a hedge down one side. Might have been anywhere in England only it wasn't. Suddenly there's a rustling in the hedgerow and a dark shape moving around. I challenge: 'Who goes there?'

"No reply and I'm taking no chances so I lunge at it with fixed bayonet. There's one hell of a squeal and a lumbering shape crosses my path. It's a huge black pig."

Locomotive on traverser ready to enter Erecting Shop, 1940

"It's a likely story," says Paddy struggling to light his pipe. "And sure there wouldn't be a deal of difference between the Hun and a pig would there now?"

Ten o'clock, Harry rings the bell, the lights dim, and after the usual "good night" banter, we stroll home along the quiet streets.

I've been transferred back to the Erecting Shop. Quite a change since I was there last. They have washing troughs now with hot and cold running water. A few minutes before the end of the shift a whistle blows and we all gather round the trough clutching a piece of evil smelling soap. You have roughly four minutes to remove the worst of the filth from your hands and wipe them on the communal towel. Still it is an improvement! At ten o'clock and three o'clock a tea cart arrives in your particular bay and you may purchase a doughnut, a scone or a sandwich, usually spam or some cheese-based spread. You can also have a cup of watery tea which tastes as if the dish cloth has been left inside the tea urn. The charge hands have tiny cabins dotted around the department into which they can retreat and concentrate upon the administration aspects of the work without the danger of being hit by a flying rivet. An ambulance centre has been set up manned regularly by qualified staff on a rota basis. You no longer need to give your number to the lavatory clerk, his services have been dispensed with — and about time too!

The unions sense they have power to bring about better working conditions but too many of our representatives are still of the boot-licking variety.

One in particular I detest. He listens to every complaint whilst washing his hands with invisible soap, goes away and does absolutely nothing about it. He is a sidesman on Sunday and occasionally preaches from a soapbox at the works entrance. During the week his main preoccupation appears to be making sketches of various locomotive parts though to what end no one has yet discovered. The rest of his time is taken up with hobnobbing with the superintendent and its rumoured that he's a Freemason.

Mind you they are not all like that and much genuine effort is being made to attempt to improve shop working conditions. Women are now being employed in the workshops especially the Machine Shop where most of the lathes are manned by them. In the Erecting Shop, however, the work is far beyond their capacity and they are reduced to fetching and carrying for the tradesmen.

We apprentices have been told to moderate our language now that there are ladies about but really some of them can match us any time. Maggie for instance loves to thrust her hand deep into some apprentice boy's pockets, whilst asking him if he's read any good books lately!

Our charge hand is tall and thin with bulging blue eyes. He has narrow cheekbones upon which two spots of colour occasionally appear but for he most part he is pale and has an austere look about him that one might find in the features of an inquisitor at a Spanish tribunal.

Beneath his brown smock he wears a dark pin stripe suit, a flannel shirt with a wing collar and a narrow bootlace tie. His shoes are black and shiny.

He calls all the apprentices "Billy" and if they misbehave threatens them with "six lace holes", in short, a kick up the backside. He is a member of the High Church, worships there three times on a Sunday and is a hypocrite for the rest of the week. Of course all charge hands have their particular favourites amongst the female staff and they are nurtured accordingly. Most have the sense to leave the cabin doors open but one in particular does not and judging by the girlish giggles from within it is not difficult to imagine what is going on.

So we light a thunder flash and place it beneath the door. The reaction is not long in coming. The door flies open and a somewhat dishevelled couple appears covered in soot from the cabin roof, their eyes white and glaring in a black mask looking for all the world like two performers in a Negro Minstrel Show. The natural thing to do would be to report the incident to the foreman in which case we might have been in serious trouble, I'm sure. However, you will appreciate the dilemma facing the unfortunate pair!

At a time when we are short of staff the women for the most part do an excellent job. It seems odd to see some of the pretty little girls I knew earlier dressed in overalls and wearing a mob cap pushing trucks loaded with materials about the department. It appears to have had the added effect also of providing better working conditions, for the females are not slow to complain if something is not quite right.

Polish and Latvian staff are now being employed mostly as labourers doing menial tasks like cleaning the toilets or brushing the department floor.

"Johnny" is employed painting white lines down the centre of the working bays, the idea being to keep the middle bay clear of all materials should there be an air raid.

He has a brush with a long handle and a bucket of whitewash. The lines must be perfectly straight so he has a strip of wood with a channel down the centre to guide him.

Unfortunately, some one has placed a baulk of wood across the centre bay upon which now rests the foreman's foot as he discusses a matter with a member of staff.

Johnny is perplexed, he doesn't know quite what to do. Go round the obstacle or over it?

He decides to do the latter and paints a perfectly straight white line over the baulk, over the foreman's shiny black shoes and down the other side.

The foreman's face is purple and he utters a few choice expletives.

Johnny grins. As he says later, his English is not so good...

Chapter Eight
Half a Crown

alf a crown — what a lot you can do with it! Fivepence will buy you a pint of best bitter and a penny less ten Woodbines. Fourpence will take you to the Theatre for a two-hour show if you don't mind sitting in the "Gods" on the hard wooden seats. For the same price you can have a front row seat in the cinema, sixpence if you sit at the back. After the show you can get a twopenny Irishman — peas and chips — a glass of Vimto costs a penny.

A session at dancing school costs threepence at St. Michael's Church Hall, a copper or two more at the class establishments. For a similar outlay you can have an hour's snooker or billiards at the Alexandra Hall. The trick is to challenge someone you think you might beat and the loser pays for the table. Alternatively you might like boxing, well, there's a fair bill at the Town Hall.

Of course if you prefer outdoor activities, there's a good choice: football matches at Gresty Road every Saturday with the first team or reserves, sports meetings on summer evenings at the L.M.S. Sports Ground and cricket in the afternoons.

Sometimes we visit the cities. Manchester and Liverpool are within a short distance. It's risky, mind you. You might finish up in an air raid shelter all night and you'll almost certainly return lying on the floor of some draughty railway coach completely blacked out and at four miles per hour. Come to think of it you might not get home at all. We visited Manchester recently and arrived at Masefield station. We returned in the evening to find the station a mass of flames.

So far as travel is concerned you have a definite advantage if you are employed by the L.M.S.. You are entitled to reduced fares, this being regarded as part of your wages. The concessions are roughly one third of the cost of a third class seat — to travel to Manchester return would cost about one shilling and sixpence.

We stroll down to the Alexandra Hall. Few of the tables are occupied so we take one of the better ones near the door.

I notice him first as he pauses to chalk his cue. He is playing snooker and seems quite a decent player. The other lad is good too, potting and positioning the balls with a good deal of skill.

After they have finished we ask them to play a foursome, losers pay for the table. They agree, we lose the frame and afterwards sit chatting for a while.

Both lads are from the Rhondda and are employed by the L.M.S.. Gareth is a semi-skilled machinist and Idris a general labourer. Before the evening has passed we become quite friendly. As night falls we stroll home together promising to see each other again.

Well, after that I get to know Gareth quite well and to a lesser degree Idris, who unfortunately works shifts two till ten or six till two.

Gareth is a great one with the girls. With his looks and attractive Welsh lilt he can bring the ducks off the water all right. He's short of stature like many of his race, has brown eyes, black wavy hair and a clear complexion. He always gives the impression that he's just come out of the bath.

He's mild mannered, generous to a fault and like myself has a great love of the countryside. As time passes we become close friends.

There are several night cafés. "The Blue Door" is a favourite with the younger set. The proprietress is an Egyptian and we get to know her quite well. There's always a little extra on the plates or maybe sixpence off the bill. Unfortunately, there are always those who will make trouble and O'Leary is one of those especially when he's been drinking. For most of the meal he's been glowering and hurling abuse in our direction and now finally he rises to his feet to follow us through the door and into the street.

There are three of us, Gareth, Idris and myself. What happens next is a little confused. For the most part we ignore our tormentor's insults until he takes a well aimed kick at Gareth's backside. We are passing a stationer's shop when suddenly a fist spreads O'Leary's nose across his face and another breaks most of his front teeth. He staggers sideways into the stationer's window and with an almighty crash falls through the window to land amidst the paraphernalia of typewriters, note books, pens and pencils which are the stationer's stock in trade.

A bus screeches to a halt, whistles are blowing and a crowd is beginning to collect. We walk quickly away and within a few minutes are on the other side of the town. The circumstances concerning the accident might have been a little difficult to explain had we remained. One thing is clear, however, one of my companions certainly packs a tidy wallop.

After that we keep out of town for a while preferring to patronise some of the more rural watering holes.

Sometimes we go to Manchester and spend the afternoon at Belle Vue. There is motor cycling on a Saturday afternoons and a large pleasure park. We try the Scenic Railway, and then the Bobs, the most scary ride in Britain. We stroll round idly kicking a tin can to each other and notice that we are being watched from a nearby tea stall. A young blonde girl daintily taps the can back to us whilst the brunette looks on smiling. We join them for a cup of tea.

Both girls are employed in the mills and hail from Trafford. They have pronounced Lancashire accents. The blonde's name is Dorothy and the brunette is Rita.

Rita, to whom I somehow have become attached, is not a raving beauty but she has an attractiveness all of her own. She has freckles and there are little laughter lines around her eyes. She has something about her which is difficult to describe. Outwardly she has a quiet, warm personality but her cherry red lips and the way her coal black hair falls in ringlets to her shoulders suggests another side to her nature — one might get the impression that she is of Spanish origin and has perhaps some of the passions of that nationality.

She has become my first real girl-friend. I visit her often at week-ends and she has met my parents and stayed the night with us. Mam likes her very much but there's a cloud on the horizon. She's a practising Catholic and I'm a lapsed Methodist. I was right about the Spanish bit too — she has relatives there.

Gareth's flirtation with the blonde doesn't last. "Don't want to get tied down," he says.

Says I'm stupid to get involved and a war on! "Never know what's going to happen, boyo," he says puffing at his cigarette.

As I say, it's risky spending too much time in the city so Rita and I visit each other alternate weekends. During the week, often after a twelve-hour shift, I meet Gareth and perhaps a few other lads for a pint and an occasional game of darts or snooker.

One Saturday evening I've taken Rita to the Odeon and with half an hour to kill before her tram is due we are sitting in Piccadilly Gardens. I've made some advances and she's encouraging me to go further but someone's got to show restraint and we're both inexperienced. A blinding white light shines in our eyes, then is doused and from the gloom there emerges the most enormous policeman.

"Come on you two, out of there," he booms.

"Nice young couple like you shouldn't be in these places at night."

He takes Rita's arm. 'Your Mum will be worried to death about you, young lady. What time's your tram?'

We are shaking so much that we can hardly answer his questions. He stays with us until Rita is safely aboard the tram, and then firmly but gently leads me in the direction of London Road Station and the 10.30 p.m. train.

Needless to say we don't sit in Piccadilly Gardens any more. Perhaps that's just as well, as quite a few unsavoury characters congregate there and the policeman was quite right to move us out.

I can't help thinking though, if I'm ever in the services I shall have to cope with worse situations than that and face far greater danger. Funny, you know, romance blossoms in some strange places. Take the Erecting Shop for instance. Billy Bonns is marrying Gladys who works in the same bay. Billy's already on top of the locomotive and the crane hook is wheeling deftly around his head. Fastened to the hook is the chamberpot, suitably inscribed with an eye in the centre and the words "I see All" in bright red letters. Billy's tried several times to extricate the "jerry" but it's fastened on to the hook with wire and twine liberally soaked in grease. Confetti is falling on his head and he is being sprayed with cold water from several directions at once.

Finally, he does manage to remove the "jerry" and carries it down the ladder in triumph. At the foot of the ladder he's presented with a canteen of cutlery and the best wishes of his workmates. Then he's carried shoulder high down the bay where Gladys awaits him.

Got to hand it to Billy, it takes a lot of guts to get married these days.

You can always tell whether the news is going to be good or bad according to who is reading it. If it is Alvar Liddell or Freddie Grisewood it is almost certainly good news but if it is John Snagge, the opposite is the case. All B.B.C. News broadcasts are prefaced with the words "This is the BBC News and this is ..... reading it." The idea is to ensure that everyone knows what the announcer's voice sounds like in case the B.B.C. is ever taken over by the Germans.

The radio plays an essential part in our lives.

Not only does it provide us with the latest news from the war and home fronts but it boosts the morale of millions as they toil in the factories with programmes like "Music While You Work". It is certainly B.B.C. Radio which looms largest in the public mind, with comedians like Tommy Handley, popular singers like Vera Lynn and Gracie Fields and a host of others. Then there are the dance bands — Henry

Hall, Harry Roy, Duke Ellington and many more. Our drab evenings are made happy by a dozen different variety shows and then there's Wilf Pickles with his Quiz Show "Have a go, Joe". Not forgetting of course the more serious side with war reporters like Wynford Vaughan Thomas and Richard Dimbleby.

Films, too, like "In which we serve" and "Brief Encounter" are being shown, drawing effectively upon particular wartime themes of separation, loss and sacrifice.

It's spring again and fresh leaves are sprouting from the trees in the Park. We soon shall have Double Summer time and it will be light until 11p.m. — at least that's what they say, I can't believe it myself.

Rita and I have tea in the pavilion. From the lake there are bellows of laughter as two couples attempt to retrieve an oar that's gone adrift. The sunlight is streaming through the cafe windows and its becoming quite warm.

Rita's sister is getting married and I'm invited to the wedding. Rita's a bridesmaid and she's quite excited about it.

The fussy old priest came to see me last week. Said he wanted to talk to me about relationships and the Catholic Church. The talk turned out to be an attempt to persuade me to join the Catholic Church and to go to Mass. I must have upset a few people when they learned I'd given him a bob for charity and told him as far as the rest was concerned to bugger off! Rita doesn't know about it, I'm sure, but one day she's going to have to.

As I've said, a half crown is a useful, dependable sort of a coin. There are four to a ten shilling note, eight to a pound and 40 to the white five-pound note. Per yard, per pound and per pint the half crown is widely used in many shops. It's also favourite stake money for the punters, not too large, not too small. The trouble was Dad didn't have a half crown which was particularly annoying, since he certainly had the winner of the big race that afternoon.

Well, he cajoled and he pleaded and finally I gave way. I'd lend him the money on condition that if the horse won I would receive half the winnings but if it lost he would owe me half a crown.

Well, it won at 20:1 and we were both delighted. Half crown is a useful coin!

Chapter Nine
Fresh Winds

Occasionally we receive an airmail from my cousin next door. They're heavily censored of course but it seems that he's in the Middle East somewhere. Says he always wanted to see the mystic East but not this way. "The Flies", he says tartly, "are large enough to drink your milk". There's better news from that quarter — the Australians have captured Tobruk and the Italian Navy has been smashed at Cape Matapan. However, the Afrika Corps under Rommel is putting up a stiff resistance and there are heavy casualties on both sides.

The "Bismarck" has been sunk but we have finally lost the "Ark Royal", an aircraft carrier sent to the bottom by "Lord Haw Haw" at least a dozen times previously,

It is now reckoned that two million women have joined the Land Army and are helping to provide vital food resources. National dried milk and orange juice is available to nursing and expectant mothers. Many items though are in short supply and points rationing has been introduced generally.

Rudolf Hess, Hitler's aide, has crash-landed a Messerschmitt in Scotland on a mission to negotiate peace terms — so it is said. He has been interrogated and finally imprisoned here.

The German tyrant has now attacked Russia and Moscow has been bombed. The Russians have now become our allies and will receive all the aid we can provide.

Suddenly and without warning the Japanese have bombed Pearl Harbour and the British battleships "Repulse" and "Renown" have been sunk. Singapore falls and an entirely new phase of the war begins. The nations of the world are now locked in a titanic struggle for control of most of the planet's surface. A struggle we must win if tyranny is to be defeated and freedom and democracy preserved for generations yet to come.

Meanwhile preparations are moving ahead to open a second front in Europe and absolute secrecy about these preparations is essential.

The artists have produced a picture of a huge ear with the caption, "The Enemy is listening:" "Funf" gazes at us balefully from behind a brick wall and "The Squander Bug" is much in evidence. Mind you, we don't see much of "The Better 'Ole" type of cartoon immortalised by Bruce Bairnsfeather in the First World War. It's a different sort of war entirely.

I've been on the same doctor's panel since I was a child. It is very much a family practice. There are three doctors, all male, and the surgery takes on the name of the senior doctor. His father treated my grandparents and he has always treated my father and mother. He is a brusque individual with iron grey hair, waxed moustache and lined features. He wears pince-nez spectacles and tends to talk down to you. Apart from that he is a very good doctor and I have no reason to complain.

Mind you, you don't go to the doctor's if you can help it. The bills are quite high particularly for home visits or prolonged treatment. Up till recently bills were collected by his clerk at a couple of shillings a week or whatever you could afford to pay.

Mam's eyes aren't so good so she has purchased a pair of spectacles from Woolworths. There is an eye chart and you choose a pair that suits your purpose after consulting the chart. It's the same with the dentist, a tooth really has to ache before you apply for treatment. This can't be right and there are moves afoot within the Labour Party — should they achieve power after this is all over — to abolish such charges and bring in a free health service for all, irrespective of their ability to pay.

Strange how a war brings together the different social classes in a fight towards a common end. Here we are with Conservative, Liberal and Labour all serving in the Cabinet. We've even got a leading trades unionist representing the giant Transport Union in the Government. This would have been impossible just a few years ago. Perhaps the winds of change are really starting to blow throughout the land.

It has been suggested that I might like to join a group discussing current affairs under the auspices of the local branch of the Workers Educational Association. As well as short W.E.A. courses in a variety of subjects they do three-year tutorials along with the Universities in subjects like Politics, Philosophy, Literature and Psychology. The fees are within the bounds of what an ordinary person is likely to be able to afford. The trouble is I work most evenings until eight o'clock. Nevertheless I do join a twenty-four lecture course in current affairs.

It's strange to be behind a desk again after so many years but I join in the debate readily enough. The tutor must think me incredibly naive as I trot out my pet theories — in fact he has almost as good as said so. Never mind, that's what I'm here for and unlike N.C.L.C. correspondence courses these lectures give me the opportunity to explore many different avenues of thought, many of which have never occurred to me.

There are several hotels in or on the outskirts of town. We visit one and are surprised to see the sign "Gentleman's Rooms". We go inside and the atmosphere is frosty. These rooms are used by businessmen, professional types, a skittering of lower management from the L.M.S. and the occasional foreman. Such rooms were used at one time for the hiring and firing of staff from the Railway Works.

The proprietor suggests we would be happier in the bar or at best the lounge but we refuse to budge. In fact after a while one old buffer actually condescends to talk to us. It's still there, you how, this "them and us" syndrome, even in the middle of a "bloody war".

The Labour Party are making sweeping gains in local elections and it won't be long before they completely control the town. Many of the new councillors are self-educated men who have risen from the ranks through the trades unions or the more intellectually minded from organisations such as the W.E.A. and other educational bodies.

Today we have our first glimpse of the enemy as a small party of captured German airmen is paraded through the town en route to a nearby prisoner-of-war camp.

Clad in the green uniforms of the Luftwaffe and escorted by soldiers from the Cheshire Regiment with fixed bayonets they are an arrogant bunch. Defiantly they sing the Herst Wessel song as they march smartly along and some even attempt to goose-step and give the Hitler salute until a jab with a bayonet warns them that such behaviour will not be tolerated. A small section of the crowd start to cat-call but for the most part we watch silently as they are led away.

Some Italian prisoners-of-war are already employed in the Railway workshops and wear a brown uniform with a yellow patch on their backs. Unlike the Germans they show no arrogance but seem glad to be out of the war.

Many speak tolerable English and make efforts to be friendly. It is difficult to work with someone who only a few short months ago was your enemy but somehow they become part of the everyday scene and though at first they are treated with reserve it soon disappears and we share a joke together. One thing we appear to have in common is a detestation of Mussolini and even more a hatred of the Germans.

One Saturday Gareth and I board a train to Manchester where we hope to watch Manchester City in a league game. The plan is that I will watch the match and see Rita later in the evening. We have a compartment to ourselves, until just as the train is about to start we are joined by two red caps and a hatless khaki-clad figure who sit opposite us.

The way in which they enter the compartment intrigues me. They shuffle in a sidelong fashion and sit down together as one. The two red caps sit tight-lipped and silent but the person between them strikes up a conversation almost at once. Football is the main topic. I note that he has a very definite accent which I can't place and appears to have a difficulty with his W's.

At Chelford, they move out in the same sidelong fashion and it isn't until then that we realise that the hatless individual is handcuffed to the other two and he has a distinctive green patch on his back. There is a very large German prisoner of war camp at Chelford.

Chapter Ten
Relationships

There's no mistaking those broad shoulders and the squat figure of the man standing by the bar. What is odd about it is that he's wearing a naval uniform. He turns towards the window and recognition dawns at once. His face takes on a huge grin and then he's beside me pumping my hand and slapping me on the back. It's Billy all right and the years slip away as I remember him lying at the foot of the oak tree puffing at his cigarette and contemplating the future on that fateful first day of the war.

As the shock of seeing each other again subsides he peers at me over the rim of his glass.

"Guess you never expected to see me in this outfit!" he grins. "Suppose you're wondering about the sea-sickness bit?

"Well, three days out and I'm prostrate. Never really get over it. I'm serving in frigates now — the buggers have a flat bottom and they wallow through the water like an old sea-cow. Great life, though, the Navy — always wanted to see the world. I think I must have seen most of it now."

He calls for two more pints.

"Seen Tich lately?"

"Missing, presumed killed," I tell him and there is a suggestion of moisture at the corner of his eye.

We stay until the landlord calls "time", laughing and talking about the past and contemplating the future. Then we stroll home together and have a bite of supper. It's midnight before he leaves and he'll be joining his ship again tomorrow.

I watch him as he leaves, his trousers flapping against his boots with the peculiar rolling gait of all naval personnel. At the corner he turns to wave and then is gone. I wonder whether I shall ever see him again.

A batch of locomotives from the Middle East has arrived for repair. They are austerity locos, large black freight. You have to be careful when you remove the boiler plates. All sorts of insects and reptiles have found a home behind them seeking warmth. The thing to do is to remove the plates with a crane hook and cable. As you do so the things come crawling out. Snakes with vivid coloured markings, tarantulas, scorpions and tiny Black Widows with a bite that can prove fatal. You have to be ready with the hose pipe and a forked stick to catch the snakes.

Johnny has come to work alongside us. He's fought for both sides, first with the Germans and then with the Russians before escaping to the West. He's got two lots of bullets in his backside so you know which way he was travelling at the time.

We tell him all about the Depression years and how bad it was. He smiles wryly and says: "I bet you've never eaten horse-shit soup." He produces a photograph of his son who's serving in the Red Army. We remark how smart he is but Johnny doesn't think so, he's disowned him and draws a finger across his throat in a gesture of disgust. Johnny is Latvian and of peasant stock. He'll never go back home, not even after it's all over.

They're so short of skilled labour that they're upgrading some of the older apprentices long before they reach the statutory age of twenty-one. I'm in the first batch and am interviewed by the Superintendent to see whether or not I'm capable of doing a journey-man's job.

I receive the rate but am not entitled to the bonus. I do, however, receive the green Union card which entitles me to work anywhere as a skilled craftsman. I am allocated a young woman as an apprentice. She's a very slight girl, blonde and pale faced with a figure that looks as if she were to eat an apple it would show. And that is exactly what happens when, after associating with certain members of the staff, she becomes pregnant. She blames the thickening of her waistline upon drinking too much Guinness but we all know different.

She's climbing a ladder one day when the Superintendent notices her condition.

"Tell that young woman to come down," he says. "She's in an interesting condition."

"It's not my fault," I reply tartly.

"Never said it was, you cheeky young devil!" he replies.

She comes down the ladder and is escorted to the office. That is the last we see of her.

I am joined later by a young male apprentice and I'm not sorry about that.

There is mixed news from abroad. The Germans are advancing into Russia. Kharkov has been captured and they stand at the gates of Stalingrad. The Afrika Corps under Rommel has recaptured

Tobruk and there is fierce fighting in the African desert. The Americans have destroyed eleven Japanese warships off the Solomon Islands.

Coventry has been bombed heavily and we have retaliated with a 1,000-bomber raid on Cologne. Daylight bombing of the Ruhr has commenced with notable effects. We have the consolation now that we know that though we are often kept from our beds with what virtually amounts to nuisance raids the Germans are now suffering the same fate.

I continue to visit Rita in Manchester but do not have the same enthusiasm. I wait at Piccadilly but she fails to appear. I know I should go to Trafford to find out what is wrong but I catch the next train home instead.

A tearful letter arrives telling me that she has not been well. Instead of commiserating I am seeking excuses to end the affair. I reply intimating that perhaps it would be better if we did not see each other for a while. My mind is in turmoil, she is a lovely person and I don't want to hurt her and yet what else can I do? I feel that I really do not want to be tied down at so young an age and then there's all this other business about Catholicism.

Finally, her Mother writes to me, sharply critical but not unkindly asking me to state my intentions. I see this as the last straw and refuse to reply. So far as I am concerned that is where the matter rests and I intend to seek new horizons. But now there comes a period when my heart is racked with pain and doubts assail my mind as to the way I have dealt with this situation. I think of that quiet home loving girl who for the past two years has been at my side and seldom far from my mind. That I have behaved abominably is true. I have received condemnation from Mam and even Gareth has criticised me saying I never should have let it run on for so long. It has never been in my nature to hurt people and I feel I have deeply wronged her. I am inclined to write to her asking forgiveness but pride forbids me. Love is like a drug and the withdrawal symptoms have within them a bitter, traumatic experience. At this moment I vow never to become emotionally involved with anyone ever again. But instinctively I know that this can never be so and that our desires for love and companionship can never be stifled and will remain with us always.

Autumn evenings and under a canopy of stars Gareth and I stroll home from some quiet inn in the country after having spent an hour by the fireside and enjoyed a pleasant chat with the locals.

The White Lion at Weston - familiar to the author when he was young

You can hardly imagine that there is a war on. The countryside smells just as sweet as it always did, the fireflies flicker across your path, a rabbit scuttles in the hedgerow, the birds sing an evening serenade. It's all so peaceful it's difficult to imagine that in a dozen different war zones men are fighting and dying for the cause they hold dear and far away their families hope and pray for their safe return.

We saw some G.I.s in town recently. Some say they are "overpaid, overfed, oversexed and over here" but they don't seem a bad crowd to me. We were talking to a couple of coloured boys and one told me that his father was once employed in Liverpool's dockland.

We meet a couple of girls at the corner of the road and Gareth with his usual wit and charm engages one in conversation. The other edges closer so that I have a whiff of her perfume. She starts to prattle on about the most absurd trivialities so I turn on my heel and walk away.

"Ignorant bugger!" she calls after me but by that time I'm almost at the gate.

Sally Knock-Knock and Dot and Carry are doing a roaring trade with the Yanks in town. There's a regular procession of them visiting the little terraced house in the cul-de-sac across the way. Slack Alice isn't doing too badly either. She takes her customers round the back of the Market of an evening.

There's a story going around that one delighted client paid her with a pile of "OMO" coupons. He was fortunate to get away with it, she has been known to fracture a customer's jaw if he didn't cough up.

We took a week's holiday earlier this year, unpaid of course, and on a rota system, one half of the factory at a time, which gives them a chance to do some very much needed maintenance work. We have one free pass a year and can travel anywhere on the L.M.S. railway system. We chose to visit Blackpool.

You are required to take your identity cards with you, national as well as L.M.S.. You must, of course, take your ration cards to be handed to the landlady on arrival and you must have also your gas mask and tin hat.

Mrs. Grey met us at the door and appraised us over pince-nez spectacles. She delivered a lecture as to how this was a well-run establishment with meals taken at the proper time and how we must keep our rooms clean and tidy and be in for ten in an evening. No self-respecting person, she argued, would wish to be on the streets after that time. We were too tired to argue and we meekly accepted the one key she proffered between the four of us.

We spent the afternoon on the beach stretched out in deckchairs. The sun was warm, seagulls shrieked and weaved overhead and what little breeze there was barely rippled the waves.

A group of children were playing on the sands or being taken for donkey rides. We noted their accents: they were almost certainly evacuees from the South.

We bought a plate of shrimps and sampled the icecream. Afterwards we bought a beach ball and kicked it around for a while. Then it was time for tea.

Several others were in the dining room, mostly elderly folk. They looked up as we came in and one white-haired old fellow sniffed disapprovingly.

The meal was served — two sardines with a couple of lank lettuce leaves and a plate of bread and margarine. For a sweet, two peach halves and a blob of cream and afterwards a tiny slice of fruit cake. To wash it down there was a cup of watery tea.

Gareth made no comment but I could see he was seething.

We spent the evening in the Tower Ballroom and marvelled at the mighty organ as it rose from the floor to provide the music for the evening's dancing. We chatted a few girls up, had some drinks and a plate of spam sandwiches and then strolled along the darkened promenade to our lodgings.

The sky was like velvet and a cool breeze ruffled our hair as we walked. We paused to enjoy a cigarette and it could only have been just after 10.30p.m. when we arrived at the digs.

The place was in darkness as one would expect but the key when inserted failed to turn in the lock. It was quite obviously locked from the inside. We knocked several times without response and then hammered on the door. Several passers by stared curiously as we strove to gain admission.

After repeated attempts the door was finally opened and there stood Mrs. Grey in her nightdress. As we moved into the hall we could see her face was livid as she angrily pointed out that it was a quarter to eleven and we must know that the door was locked at ten o'clock prompt, and that she had had to rise from her bed to let us in. She would talk to us about it in the morning. Gareth' s face was blood red.

"You'll talk about it now, Mrs Grey," he said. "We'll pay you for what we've had, little as it is, collect our bags, if you please, together with our ration cards and we'll be on our way. Tomorrow we will report you to the Hotels and Boarding Houses Association and I don't think they are going to be at all pleased."

I was getting worried. I thought she was going to have apoplexy but she finally sat down on a chair and calmed down. She'd had a shock and we pressed our advantage. Suddenly she was all apologies, promising that things would improve and the door would in future be left on the latch. It was too late to argue further so we went up to our rooms. She came in next morning and gave us a coy glance and served us with a reasonable breakfast. After that things did improve. I wouldn't say though that it was the best place I'd ever stayed in.

For the most part we enjoyed our stay in Blackpool. The weather remained fine for almost the whole of the week and we returned home sporting a sun tan and with a new will to face whatever we must in the months ahead.

Chapter Eleven
Glimpses

The war which many thought would last a few short months drags on into another year. The shortages coupled with long hours in the factory are starting to take their toll though morale generally remains high.

The younger you are the better you are able to stand the strain. Amongst us there is a growing optimism that after all this is over the world will somehow become a better place to live in. Such optimism is not always shared by older folk, especially those who experienced the First World War and its grim aftermath.

Those whose task it is to direct the war effort in the factory have discovered there is a growing malaise that sometimes results in a breakdown in health. Two incidents that demonstrate this have occurred recently.

An elderly but nevertheless conscientious foreman has been discovered in the cemetery, bowler-hatted, whistle in hand, directing a non-existent crane to deliver its burden into an open grave. Another has been seen white-faced and perspiring, frenziedly chasing the "Squander Bug" around the locomotive bays.

The incidents, regarded by some as being extremely funny, do on sober reflection demonstrate the dire effects upon the civilian population of prolonged conflict.

The fear of invasion has receded and we spend less time in the shelters. There is, however, a growing impatience to open a second front in Europe. That plans are afoot to do this we are sure, but information is naturally scarce and careless talk which could hazard such plans is to be avoided at all costs.

This Christmas we have a concert in the workshops. The West End Silver Band entertains us with a programme of light music. We sing "Roll out the Barrel", "Coming Home on a Wing and a Prayer" and the "White Cliffs of Dover". The Minister from Christ Church conducts the carol service and we conclude with a prayer for peace.

The younger apprentices engage in the traditional "Sticky Bun Competition". The buns, well laced with treacle, are suspended on a piece of string at intervals along a central wooden beam. The apprentices, hands behind their backs, must attempt to consume the bun, drink a bottle of pop, and finally blow up and burst a balloon. The whole thing is quite uproarious and the victor certainly earns his certificate of merit and a small prize for his efforts.

The Superintendent, hatless and a little flushed, addresses the huge crowd and wishes us all a Merry Christmas and thanks us all for our efforts during the past year.

The winter that follows is long and hard but at last it is spring again and with it the promise of a new beginning.

In the Queens Park and Jubilee Gardens the grass is fresh and green. The flower beds are ablaze with colour. Sweet scented wallflowers joust with tall tulips standing erect like soldiers on parade and on the banks beside the stream a host of golden daffodils nod to each other in the soft breeze.

Strolling along those tranquil paths amongst so much beauty it is difficult to imagine that we are at war and that all over the world millions of people are fighting and dying in the cause of freedom to enjoy the simple things of life that hitherto in the crass ignorance of youth we have taken for granted. As we gaze around us we are conscious of the awesome responsibility that is ours to ensure that this dreadful thing shall never happen again and that future generations may learn to live in peace and harmony together.

As spring gives way to summer the radio tells us that the Germans are now in full retreat from the Caucasus, and the Don Valley. After the long months the siege of Stalingrad has been lifted and the Russians, after suffering appalling casualties, are now on the offensive. Many thousands of German soldiers have frozen to death in the Russian Winter and thousands more have now surrendered to the victorious Russian Army.

Tripoli has been captured by the Eighth Army and Sicily has been invaded by Allied forces. The Italian mainland has been penetrated and Mussolini overthrown. German troops have now occupied Rome.

The Americans are launching daylight raids on Germany whilst in the Far East they have had notable victories in the Solomon Islands and Guadalcanal. At sea they have inflicted heavy losses on the Japanese fleet.

At home they have received a mixed welcome. We still nurture a resentment that they have waited until now to come to our aid and then only after they themselves were attacked at Pearl Harbour. Nevertheless, we are grateful for the aid we receive and that we no longer stand alone in the fight against tyranny.

Dora, my cousin from next door, is home for a spot of leave. She looks very smart in her A.T.S. uniform and she now has two stripes on her sleeve. She's getting married shortly to a grocer from Chislehurst and has invited us to the wedding.

The Germans are now using guided missiles to bomb Southern towns and cities, particularly London. These frightful weapons, first V-1s and then V-2s, are directed indiscriminately against the civilian population. We shall need to seek out their bases and destroy them.

My home town boasts some 60 public houses and hotels. In addition to these there are several Workingmen's Clubs. Some are politically orientated like the Conservative, Liberal and Labour Clubs. Others like the Pioneer Anglers and the Western Sports Club cater for a wide range of sporting interests both indoor and outdoor.

Some also provide educational venues for such organisations as the W.E.A. and cater for a wide range of other interests. Their main attraction to many is that they provide cheap beer and live entertainment particularly at weekends. Because of its close proximity to canals and rivers the main sporting interest in the town is angling and during the season numerous fishing matches are held mostly on Saturday afternoons.

The railway workshops also hold annual fishing matches. For some it is a serious business, for others an opportunity to escape from the factories and enjoy a pleasant afternoon in the countryside with perhaps a drink and a sing-song at the local during the evening. Prizes in reducing value according to the weight of the catch provide an incentive and the presentation is usually made on the Monday

Annual fishing match, Belle Vue Hotel, Earle Street, Crewe

evening following the match. The families are invited to these gatherings and enjoy a pleasant social evening.

One such fishing match I attended almost ended in disaster.

Halfway to our destination it was suddenly realised that we had forgotten to bring the scales to weigh the fish. A member was delegated to return home by taxi to retrieve the scales. He took a considerable time during which the rest of the party enjoyed the hospitality offered at a local inn. The result was that on arrival at the canal several members of the party were somewhat inebriated.

It had been raining and the canal banks were steep and slippery — so much so that in their haste to find a suitable spot two members slid ever so gently, I thought, into the canal which at that spot was quite deep. The unfortunate pair spent the rest of the afternoon in their underpants whilst their clothes dried out on the bank.

Luckily the sun appeared from behind a cloud and for the duration of the match it was quite warm, but Cecil had lost his spectacles and was blind without them. He constantly reminded us that if we caught a perch with spectacles on it was very definitely his!

Tea was served at the local hotel and afterwards we spent the evening enjoying a few pints of best bitter and a sing-song around the piano until it was time to depart.

The coach was in darkness except for two small blue light bulbs which shed a ghostly light on the interior. We chatted for a while and a small party played cards at the rear of the coach with the aid of a pocket torch.

The disaster struck as the call of nature came upon us and we implored the driver to stop the bus.

There was a sudden lurch as the driver sought a suitable spot, the emergency doors at the rear of the coach opened wide and one of the card-playing fraternity disappeared into the gloom. Some few hundred yards further on we ground to a halt.

We walked back along the road and eventually discovered Eddie, cards still clutched in his hands, sitting bolt upright in the middle of the road. He was a little bemused but otherwise unhurt and insisted that he had a winning hand.

No-one realised that the coach was parked on a bridge bounded by a low stone wall. The result was that several of the party dived over the wall into the bushes down below and had some difficulty in extricating themselves from the undergrowth. Furthermore, the ground below the bridge sloped steeply to the centre and one unfortunate chap fell some 15 feet into the branches of a tree and suffered a fractured arm, as we later discovered.

A somewhat chastened bunch of anglers arrived back in the town that evening!

Chapter Twelve
Crossroads

The gaunt red brick building stood on what was then the out-skirts of the town. It was surrounded by a high wall on all sides and access was through wrought iron gates and up a short drive to the main hall. In a nearby field there was a tethered barrage balloon.

Scarlet fever and diphtheria were common in those days and sometimes reached epidemic proportions. The hospital was purpose built to deal with such cases. Typhoid and enteric fever were also treated there.

I had suffered scarlet fever whilst still at school but had been unable to gain admittance to the hospital because of the vast number of cases to be dealt with and had had to be nursed at home. My asso-ciation with the hospital came about in a very different fashion.

Gareth and I had enjoyed a George Formby film at the Palace Cinema and were returning home when we spied two attractive young ladies walking in the same direction. We emitted a few wolf-whistles and they paused to stand in a shop doorway. We spoke to them and they replied with some saucy remarks in the Welsh lan-guage. Gareth, of course, understood and replied with some vigour. Nonplussed at first they then burst into fits of laughing and soon were conversing quite freely, but this time in English.

The scent of disinfectant was strong about them and I enquired if they were in fact nurses. They replied in the affirmative and I was a little shocked to learn that they were employed at the Isolation Hospital. Apparently all the nurses there were Welsh including the Matron.

We accompa-nied them back to the Hospital and

The Fever Ambulance, used for Isolation Hospital patients. Picture kindly loaned by Mrs S A Williams

The Isolation Hospital, which was opened in 1897. It stood in five acres of land North of Middlewich Street. (Photograph by kind permission of John Mayman, Mayor's Attendant).

promised to take them to the Theatre the following evening.

Myfanwy was tall, robust, with rosy cheeks and laughing brown eyes. By contrast, Moira was pale and slim, with dark hair and a more serious disposition. She came from Anglesey and was of farming stock. Her father owned the riding school on the cliffs overlooking Liverpool Bay.

After a while I found myself falling madly in love with her. Sometimes on cold evenings we would snuggle together beside the Hospital gates and plan what we would do after the war was over. At holiday times I would travel home with her to Anglesey and stay in the little whitewashed cottage overlooking the sea.

We would watch the merchant ships entering and leaving the bay. We had a special interest since her brother was a merchant seaman employed by the Elder Dempster Line.

Gareth's affair with Myfanwy was far more tempestuous. He had been ill lately, a heart problem, the doctor thought. I think he realised that a firm relationship was not to be. Anyway the romance fizzled out and was rekindled a dozen times or more during the time I knew him.

Nurses' wages at that time were desperately poor: £2 10s a month and scrub the floors as well as nursing duties.

Moira left my home town to take up general nursing at Manchester Royal Infirmary. After qualifying as an S.E.A.N. she earned a magnificent sum of £12 10s a month. To take her S.R.N. she moved to Stoke City General Hospital and earned there £17 a month as a fully qualified nurse.

The war and the constant moving about disrupted our relationship and after she had taken a post at Bangor, North Wales, I decided that that was enough — she was married to nursing and there could be no future for us. We parted by mutual consent and she returned my ring, but we continued to write to each other.

Three nurses from the Isolation Hospital pictured in their distinctive uniform. Apparently they were all Welsh, including the Matron. Photograph kindly loaned by Mrs S A Williams

There were several affairs after that but none of a serious nature. I felt I was being watched by some of the other nurses at the Isolation Hospital and that Moira knew exactly what was going on.

Soon there is a momentous announcement. A second front has opened up in Europe. There is fierce fighting, stiff resistance and heavy casualties, but after months of attack and counter attack France is liberated by the Allied advance.

Our forces, amidst scenes of great jubilation, enter Paris. Rome falls and Mussolini is hanged together with his mistress from a wooden beam in the centre of the city. The Italians spit upon the corpses.

In the Middle East the Afrika Corps under Rommel has been routed by the forces of Field Marshal Montgomery of the Eighth Army. Soon Allied forces, Russian, American and British, form a pincer movement and move forward into Germany itself. They stand at the gates of Berlin itself as the Fuhrer dies in a bunker along with his mistress, Eva Braun.

The war in Europe is moving into its final stages and after the

German surrender is signed on Luneberg Heath a date is set to celebrate V.E. Day.

And now the irony of fate takes a hand and the past returns to
haunt me.

Moira and I have agreed to settle our differences and she is to visit
me on Saturday. My heart races at the thought. I return home from
work on Friday evening to be greeted by Gareth, who almost unable
to contain himself tells me that Rita is waiting at home to see me.

Now here's a pretty kettle of fish! Mam and Dad have little sym-
pathy for me as I walk into the tiny kitchen fervently hoping that the
floor will open to swallow me.

Rita rises to greet me. She is in W.R.N.S. uniform and is as smart
as paint. Mixed emotions surge through my body in rapid succession
and I feel cheap, unworthy and ashamed.

It's hard, terribly hard, but a decision must obviously be made.
Finally clean and suitably refreshed I take her out for the evening.

There's a tearful reunion and finally I take her to the station, to
join the last train to Manchester.

We embrace for the last time and she waves as the train slowly
leaves the station.

Moira arrives early the following morning.

For a brief moment we just stand and look at each other without
speaking. The suddenly, oblivious of the crowds that mill around us,
she is in my arms and our cheeks are wet with tears as we leave the
platform together.

Later we stroll together in the Park beside the lake and I place the
ring back on her finger. She does not know and can never know the
trauma of the previous evening. The decision has been made and now
there is no turning back. Later as we plan for our future I know that
the decision is a right one.

As we leave the Park the sun appears from behind the clouds and
somehow the world seems a better place.

We celebrate V.E. Day together. There are street parties, singing
and dancing in the streets. The bells are ringing, the streets are
adorned with garlands, and everywhere we witness the mad wild
abandon of thousands of people almost hysterical with delight as they
celebrate this truly wonderful day.

In the evening we sit holding hands in a country inn on the outskirts of the town and our hearts are glad now that the war is over at
last and we can begin to plan our lives together.

For many months, however, the Japanese campaign continues until finally atom bombs are dropped on Hiroshima and Nagasaki and the war in the Far East at last ends in victory for our forces. Again we celebrate — this time V.J. Day.

The victory is tinged with sadness. My cousin has returned a broken man. Billy will not be coming home and many friends and relations I shall see no more. Thus is the tragedy of war.

Our relief is profound that we have rid the world of tyranny but we can never know that with the advent of nuclear weapons we will face a new threat and that one day a fragile peace will be preserved on a balance of terror and the fear of nuclear holocaust.

But that is another story.

Index

List of illustrations

**An imprint of
ANNE LOADER
PUBLICATIONS**

**Other books published by the Léonie Press, an imprint of
Anne Loader Publications, 13 Vale Road, Hartford,
Northwich, Cheshire CW8 1PL, Gt Britain, include:**

Memories of a Cheshire Childhood by Lenna Bickerton
(ISBN 1 901253 00 7), price £4.99

A House with Sprit: A dedication to Marbury Hall
by Jackie Hamlett and Christine Hamlett (ISBN 1 901253 01 5),
price £8.99

Kathleen: Memories of a girl who grew up in wartime
by K M Thomas (ISBN 1 901253 02 3), price £4.99

*Of Those Who Lie in Foreign Fields: In remembrance of the men
of Colton who served but did not return* by Sqn Ldr R L Stanley
MBE and Joy Bratherton (ISBN 1 901253 03 1), price £6.99

Who says you are there no more? by G C Kanjilal
(ISBN 1 901253 04 X), price £6.95

*Ulu Tiram: A cameo of life in Malaya at the time of 'The
Emergency'* by Peter Thomas and Kathleen Thomas
(ISBN 1 901253 05 8), price £5.75

*A Bull by the Back Door: How an English family find their own
paradise in rural France* by Anne Loader
(ISBN 1 901253 06 6), price £8.99